It's another Quality Book from CGP

This book is for anyone doing
GCSE Mathematics at Higher Level.

It's packed with tricky functional questions designed
to make you sweat — because that's the only way
you'll get any better.

It's also got some daft bits in to try and make
the whole experience at least vaguely
entertaining for you.

What CGP is all about

Our sole aim here at CGP is to produce the highest
quality books — carefully written, immaculately presented
and dangerously close to being funny.

Then we work our socks off to get them
out to you — at the cheapest possible prices.

Contents

Published by Coordination Group Publications Ltd.

Editors:
Katie Braid, Rosie Gillham, David Ryan, Jane Towle, Karen Wells, Dawn Wright.

Contributors:
Michael Davidson, Peter Hall, Claire Jackson, Mark Moody,
Kieran Wardell, Helen Waugh, Jeanette Whiteman.

Proofreading:
Peter Caunter and Helena Hayes.

ISBN: 978 1 84762 513 7

Height/Weight chart on front cover from The Food Standards Agency © Crown copyright reproduced under the terms of the Click-use Licence.

Groovy website: www.cgpbooks.co.uk

Printed by Elanders Ltd, Newcastle upon Tyne.
Jolly bits of clipart from CORELDRAW®

Based on the classic CGP style created by Richard Parsons.

Getting Around

Q1 Ellie and Rachel are taking part in an orienteering competition. They must navigate using a map and compass, and run in straight lines to each of the checkpoints in order.

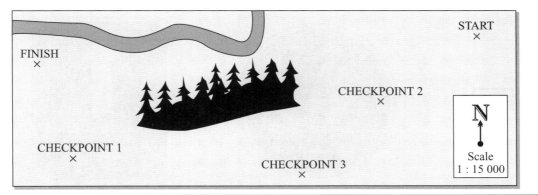

a) What distance does **1 cm** on the map represent?

b) What **bearing** should they travel on to reach the first checkpoint from the start?

c) What is the **total distance** of the orienteering course?

d) Ellie and Rachel run at about **10 km/h**. How long will it take them to complete the course?

Q2 Lydia is putting together the timetable for a new tourist train linking four lakeside villages. The service starts from Hawley and finishes at Turnbull.

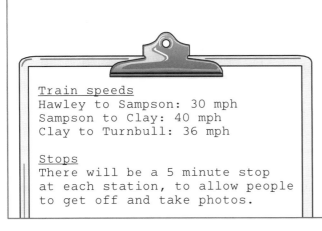

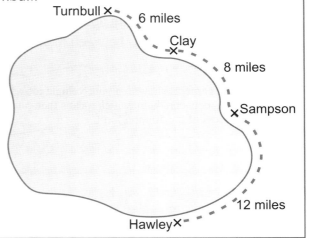

a) The first train will leave at **9.30 am**. What are the departure times for Sampson and Clay?

b) What time will the **10.00 am** train arrive in Turnbull?

Getting Around

Q3 Kieran is driving along a motorway on his way to watch a football match. The match kicks off at **7.45 pm**. He checks the time, his speed, and how far he has left to drive:

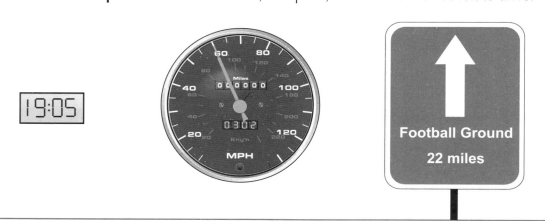

a) What **time** will Kieran arrive at the ground if he averages **60 mph** for the rest of the journey?

b) There is a **30 mph** speed limit on the last **4 miles** of the journey. What is the minimum average speed Kieran needs to drive at **before** then to get to the ground **15 minutes before** kick off? Give your answer to the nearest mph.

Q4 Kieran receives a letter saying that he has been caught speeding on a 50 mph section of the motorway by a pair of average speed cameras.

The cameras are **2500 m** apart and the time taken for a car to pass between them is recorded.

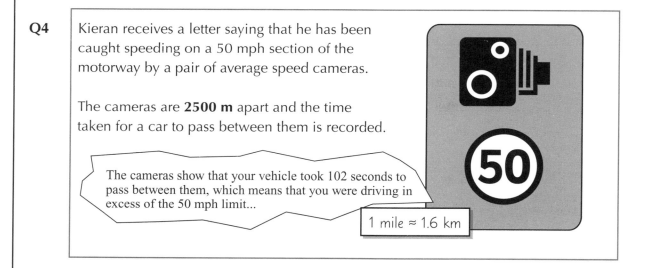

The cameras show that your vehicle took 102 seconds to pass between them, which means that you were driving in excess of the 50 mph limit...

1 mile ≈ 1.6 km

a) Kieran thinks the calculation of his speed is wrong.
From the time recorded, what was Kieran's average speed between the cameras, in **mph**?

b) If Kieran had been travelling within the speed limit, what is the **minimum time** it should have taken him to pass between the cameras, to the nearest second?

Getting Around

Q5 Francois is planning a business trip to the UK from France.
Francois will arrive at Plymouth, drive to his three meetings and then return to Plymouth.

Distances between towns/cities (miles)*
        *1 mile ≈ 1.6 km

Bristol

84	Exeter		
194	110	Penzance	
125	44	77	Plymouth

9.00 am meeting in Exeter (1 hour),
11.30 am meeting in Bristol (hour and a half),
4.30 pm meeting in Penzance (1 hour).

FERRY TIMES
Plymouth to Roscoff, France

Departure times:
18.45, 19.30, 20.30, 21.45.

a) Francois can claim travel expenses from his company of **€0.65** per kilometre travelled.
How much will he be able to claim from his business trip? Give your answer in **Euros**.

b) If Francois drives at an average of **60 mph**, which ferry should he book home from Plymouth?

Q6 Francois needs to hire a car for his business trip.
He has a choice of the two cars shown below:

1 gallon ≈ 4.5 litres
1 mile ≈ 1.6 km

COMPANY POLICIES

Car hire
Please keep company costs to a
minimum by hiring the most efficient
car and by driving economically.
Travel expenses will otherwise
not be covered by the company.

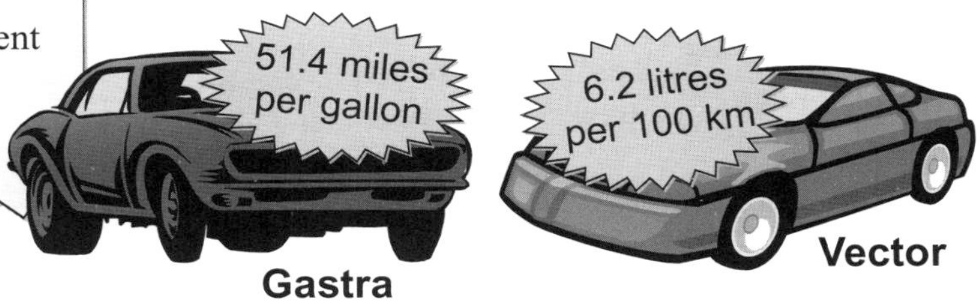

51.4 miles
per gallon

Gastra

6.2 litres
per 100 km

Vector

Which car should Francois hire?

Getting Around

Q7 The Bromley Abbots theme park is unveiling a new ride. They want to use a velocity-time graph to advertise the speed and acceleration of the new ride.

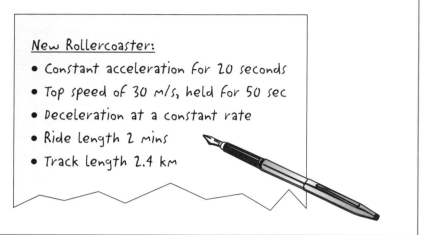

New Rollercoaster:
- Constant acceleration for 20 seconds
- Top speed of 30 m/s, held for 50 sec
- Deceleration at a constant rate
- Ride length 2 mins
- Track length 2.4 km

Draw a **velocity-time graph** for the theme park to use in their advertising of the new ride.

Q8 Melanie is planning a school trip for **25** students from her English class to see a play in Teksbury. She will drive the old school minibus, which runs on **diesel** and averages 32 miles per gallon.

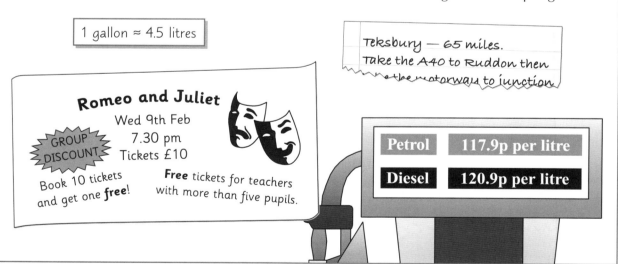

1 gallon ≈ 4.5 litres

Teksbury — 65 miles.
Take the A40 to Ruddon then
the motorway to junction

Romeo and Juliet
Wed 9th Feb
7.30 pm
Tickets £10

GROUP DISCOUNT

Book 10 tickets and get one **free**!

Free tickets for teachers with more than five pupils.

Petrol	117.9p per litre
Diesel	120.9p per litre

What is the **minimum amount** each student should pay for the trip to cover all the costs? Give your answer to the nearest 10p.

Food and Drink

Q1 June is buying food and drink to make packed lunches for her youth club's day trip.
Everyone going had to choose from different options for their lunch:

Packed Lunch Choices:

Bread Rolls	White	29	Brown	21
Filling	Cheese	32	Ham	18
Drink	Cola	13	Lemonade	37

Each person needs:
1 roll, 1 slice of ham or cheese, and 250 ml drink.

a) How many **packs** of each type of bread roll should June buy?

b) How many **bottles** of each type of drink should she buy?

c) June mistakenly only buys 5 packets of cheese slices. She knows that around a **third** of the club are vegetarian. Will there be enough cheese for the vegetarians?

Q2 June also wants to bake some flapjacks to put in the packed lunches.
She thinks that **three** of her baking trays, shown below, should be enough to make **50** flapjacks.

Simple Flapjack Recipe
(Makes one tray of size 20 cm × 20 cm × 5 cm)

250 g oats   150 g butter
75 g sugar   75 g syrup

Melt ingredients together in a saucepan.
Spread into baking tray and bake in oven...

June's baking trays
(size 20 cm × 20 cm × 2.5 cm)

a) What quantity of each ingredient will June need to use to fill **three** of her tins?

b) How should June divide up the flapjack so there's at least **50** equal rectangular slices, at least **3 cm** wide, with as little left over as possible?

Food and Drink

Q3   Dawn is baking a cake, but only has a little flour left in the cupboard. She weighs out what's there, but needs to work out how much of the other ingredients are needed to make the recipe.

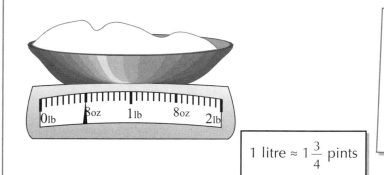

1 litre ≈ $1\frac{3}{4}$ pints

Dawn's 'Caffeine Crazy' Cake

12oz flour

9 oz butter

9 oz sugar

3 eggs

¾ pint of black filter coffee

a)   What amount of each of the other ingredients does Dawn need?

b)   Dawn's measuring jug only has a scale for **millilitres**.
Approximately how many ml of coffee does she need?

Q4   Dawn has a 'fan-assisted' electric oven with a temperature dial in °Fahrenheit.
Her recipe tells her to bake the cake for **45 minutes** at a temperature of **180 °C**.

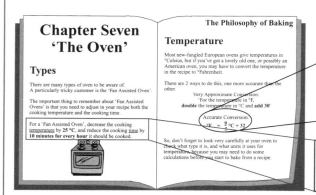

Chapter Seven 'The Oven'

Types

There are many types of oven to be aware of.
A particularly tricky customer is the 'Fan Assisted Oven'.

The important thing to remember about 'Fan Assisted Ovens' is that you need to adjust in your recipe both the cooking temperature and the cooking time.

For a 'Fan Assisted Oven', decrease the cooking <u>temperature</u> by **25 °C**, and reduce the cooking <u>time</u> by **10 minutes for every hour** it should be cooked.

The Philosophy of Baking

Temperature

Most new-fangled European ovens give temperatures in °Celsius, but if you've got a lovely old one, or possibly an American oven, you may have to convert the temperature in the recipe to °Fahrenheit.

There are 2 ways to do this, one more accurate than the other.

Very Approximate Conversion:
'For the temperature in °F,
double the temperature in °C and **add 30**'

Accurate Conversion:
°F = $\frac{9}{5}$ °C + 32

So, don't forget to look very carefully at your oven to check what type it is, and what units it uses for temperature, because you may need to do some calculations before you start to bake from a recipe.

Accurate Conversion:
$$°F = \frac{9}{5} °C + 32$$

For a 'Fan Assisted Oven', decrease the cooking <u>temperature</u> by **25 °C**, and reduce the cooking <u>time</u> by **10 minutes for every hour** it should be cooked.

a)   How **long** does Dawn need to bake the cake for? Give your answer to the nearest minute.

b)   What temperature should she set her oven to in **°F**?

Food and Drink

Q5   Jackson's family are coming over at **8 pm** for dinner.

He can either use the frozen turkey he has, or buy a fresh joint of beef when he finishes work at 5.30 pm.

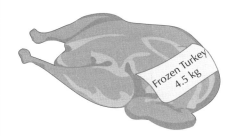

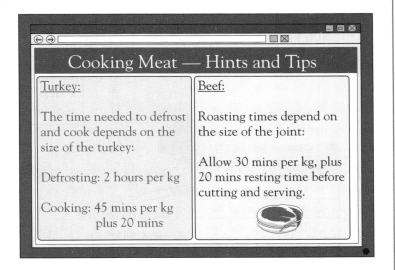

Cooking Meat — Hints and Tips

Turkey:

The time needed to defrost and cook depends on the size of the turkey:

Defrosting: 2 hours per kg

Cooking: 45 mins per kg plus 20 mins

Beef:

Roasting times depend on the size of the joint:

Allow 30 mins per kg, plus 20 mins resting time before cutting and serving.

a)   Would there be **enough time** to defrost and cook the turkey for 8 pm if Jackson takes it out of the freezer at 9.15 am before he goes to work?

b)   It should take Jackson 30 minutes to buy some beef and get home.
What is the **biggest joint** of beef, to the nearest kg, he could buy to be done for 8 pm?

Q6   Jackson asks his mum what temperature he needs to set the oven to.
His oven gives the temperature in **°C**.

To change temperature from Celsius to Fahrenheit:

$$°F = \frac{9}{5}°C + 32$$

a)   What temperature in **°C** should Jackson set his oven to?

b)   He thinks it would be useful to **simplify** the formula to convert temperatures in °F to °C approximately without needing a calculator. What formula could he use instead?

Food and Drink

Q7 Debbie has invited her friend from her slimming club round for a meal. They are allowed up to **500 kcal** per meal, so Debbie needs to check that the food she has in will be suitable.

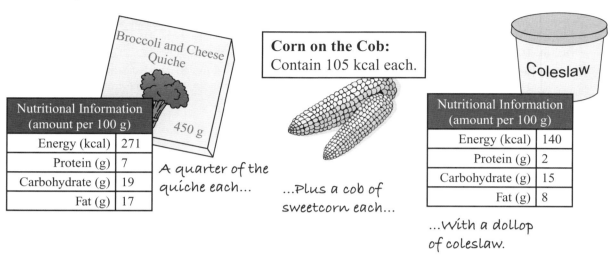

Broccoli and Cheese Quiche

450 g

Nutritional Information (amount per 100 g)	
Energy (kcal)	271
Protein (g)	7
Carbohydrate (g)	19
Fat (g)	17

A quarter of the quiche each...

Corn on the Cob: Contain 105 kcal each.

...Plus a cob of sweetcorn each...

Coleslaw

Nutritional Information (amount per 100 g)	
Energy (kcal)	140
Protein (g)	2
Carbohydrate (g)	15
Fat (g)	8

...With a dollop of coleslaw.

a) How much **coleslaw** can Debbie put on each plate and still be within the calorie limit?

b) Debbie decides to go without coleslaw so she can have more quiche.
Roughly what **fraction** of the quiche can she cut for herself?

Q8 Juanita is having a Mexican-themed party and plans to make a very large pan of chilli, with rice, tortilla chips and alcohol-free margarita cocktails. There will be **30 people** at the party in total.

Chilli Con Carne
(serves 8)

1 kg beef mince
800 g chopped tomatoes
800 g red kidney beans
2 onions
2 garlic cloves
4 tsp dried chilli flakes
1 tsp ground cumin
1 tsp ground coriander

Easy Cook Rice
Use 90 g per serving

TORTILLA CHIPS
Serves 8

Alcohol-Free Cocktails
The Margarita:
Mix real lemonade, fresh lime juice, and orange syrup in the ratio
5 : 2 : 1
Shake over ice.
(Allow 300 ml per person)

Write a list of the **amounts** of food and drink Juanita needs.

Traigan la bulla! Traigan el funk!

Shopping

Q1 John is building a shed. He looks online to find out the prices of some of the items he needs.

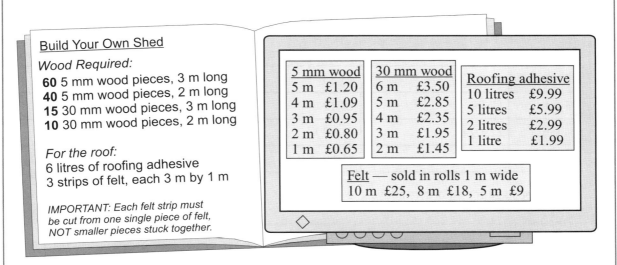

Build Your Own Shed

Wood Required:
60 5 mm wood pieces, 3 m long
40 5 mm wood pieces, 2 m long
15 30 mm wood pieces, 3 m long
10 30 mm wood pieces, 2 m long

For the roof:
6 litres of roofing adhesive
3 strips of felt, each 3 m by 1 m

IMPORTANT: Each felt strip must be cut from one single piece of felt, NOT smaller pieces stuck together.

5 mm wood		30 mm wood		Roofing adhesive	
5 m	£1.20	6 m	£3.50	10 litres	£9.99
4 m	£1.09	5 m	£2.85	5 litres	£5.99
3 m	£0.95	4 m	£2.35	2 litres	£2.99
2 m	£0.80	3 m	£1.95	1 litre	£1.99
1 m	£0.65	2 m	£1.45		

Felt — sold in rolls 1 m wide
10 m £25, 8 m £18, 5 m £9

a) What is the cheapest way for John to buy all the **adhesive** he needs?

b) What is the cheapest way for John to buy all the **felt** he needs?

c) Work out the **cost** of all the wood that John needs.

Q2 Joe's mum is checking her shopping receipt.
She thinks she may have been overcharged for one or more of the items.

```
Apples £1.69/kg
   648g          £1.32
Soft drink       £0.59
Crisps           £0.79
Crisps           £0.79
Soft drink       £0.59
 *2 for £1.10*  −£0.08
Crisps           £0.79
 *3 for £2*     −£0.16

    TOTAL        £4.63
```

a) Which item(s) has she been **overcharged** for?

b) What is the **correct total** amount she should be charged?

c) Joe's mum pays the correct amount with a **£10 note**. She gives the change to Joe and tells him to split it evenly with his three sisters. How much money should Joe give to each sister?

Shopping

Q3 Before his holiday, Andrew bought a **1 Gb** memory card for his camera from
Bestvaluememory.co.uk. He now wants a larger memory card so is looking at prices online.

Card size	Digitalmemcards.co.uk	Bestvaluememory.co.uk	Memcd.co.uk	allcostsless.co.uk
512 Mb	£5.99	£5.85	£4.89	£5.12
1 Gb	£7.99	£8.12	£6.58	£7.45
4 Gb	£19.99	£12.99	£15.99	£14.98
Postage*	£1.75	£1.50	£2.00	£1.25

*Free postage for all orders above £15.

a) Which company should Andrew use to buy a 4 Gb memory card at the **cheapest** price?

b) Bestvaluememory.co.uk says: "If you find any of our products cheaper elsewhere, we'll refund
double the difference!" How much should they **refund** Andrew for the 1 Gb card he bought?

Q4 Andrew and his sister Lisa are comparing the cost of printing some of their holiday photos.
Andrew has **55** photos to print out, and his sister wants to print **95**.

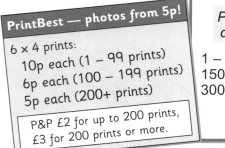

PrintBest — photos from 5p!

6 × 4 prints:
10p each (1 – 99 prints)
6p each (100 – 199 prints)
5p each (200+ prints)

P&P £2 for up to 200 prints,
£3 for 200 prints or more.

*PrintCheaper — photos
delivered the next day!*

1 – 149 prints just 11p each*
150 – 300 prints just 7p each*
300+ prints just 5p each*

*6 × 4 prints,
add £1.50 for P&P.*

CheapoPrint

Free P&P!

6 by 4 prints:

7p each (250+ prints)
8p each (100+ prints)
12p each (under 100 prints)

a) Andrew and Lisa think it will be cheaper to combine their orders.
Which company should they use to get the **cheapest** deal?

b) Andrew orders both sets of photos from the cheapest company.
How much money does Lisa owe him for her photos and half the P&P cost?

Shopping

Q5 Lina is having friends round to watch films, and wants to stock up on drinks and snacks. The supermarket has the following choices:

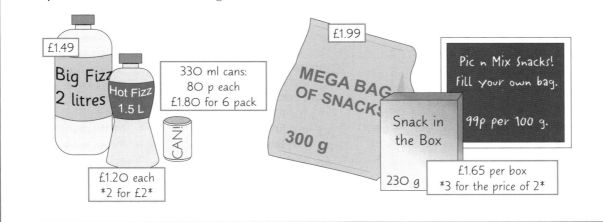

a) Which drink and snack should Lina buy to get the **best value**?

b) Lina only wants to spend **£5**. Is this possible if she chooses the best value options?

Q6 Lina notices that the supermarket has some deals on DVD films, so she decides to buy some to watch with her friends later.

Big DVD Sale!

5% off all individual sale DVDs
(usual price £12)

OR

Buy **3** and get a **FURTHER 5%** off the total

OR

Buy **5** and get a **FURTHER 10%** off the total

a) How many sale DVDs could Lina buy for **£50**?

b) Lina can get **12%** student discount on non-sale DVDs. She wants to buy **5 films**. Is it cheaper for her to choose from the sale or non-sale DVDs?

Shopping

Q7 James is a student, and wants to buy some stationery from a catalogue.
He has written a list of everything he needs.

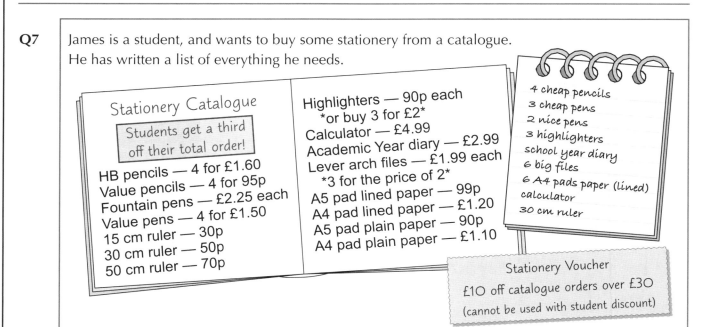

Stationery Catalogue

Students get a third off their total order!

HB pencils — 4 for £1.60
Value pencils — 4 for 95p
Fountain pens — £2.25 each
Value pens — 4 for £1.50
15 cm ruler — 30p
30 cm ruler — 50p
50 cm ruler — 70p

Highlighters — 90p each
or buy 3 for £2
Calculator — £4.99
Academic Year diary — £2.99
Lever arch files — £1.99 each
3 for the price of 2
A5 pad lined paper — 99p
A4 pad lined paper — £1.20
A5 pad plain paper — 90p
A4 pad plain paper — £1.10

4 cheap pencils
3 cheap pens
2 nice pens
3 highlighters
school year diary
6 big files
6 A4 pads paper (lined)
calculator
30 cm ruler

Stationery Voucher
£10 off catalogue orders over £30
(cannot be used with student discount)

What is the **least** James can spend to get everything he needs?

Q8 Polly is working abroad for the whole of August, so has asked her sister
Harriet to look after her **two dogs**, **three cats** and **seven goldfish**.

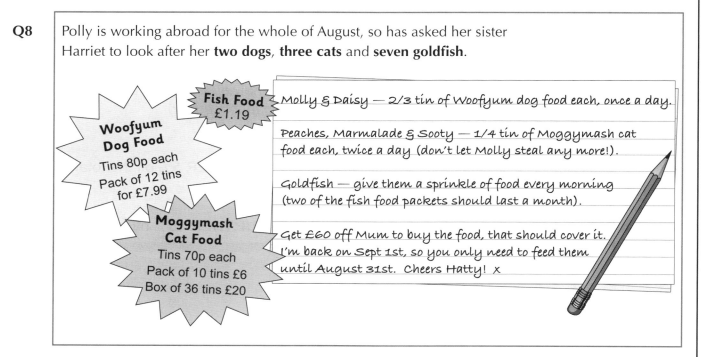

Fish Food
£1.19

Woofyum
Dog Food
Tins 80p each
Pack of 12 tins
for £7.99

Moggymash
Cat Food
Tins 70p each
Pack of 10 tins £6
Box of 36 tins £20

Molly & Daisy — 2/3 tin of Woofyum dog food each, once a day.

Peaches, Marmalade & Sooty — 1/4 tin of Moggymash cat food each, twice a day (don't let Molly steal any more!).

Goldfish — give them a sprinkle of food every morning (two of the fish food packets should last a month).

Get £60 off Mum to buy the food, that should cover it. I'm back on Sept 1st, so you only need to feed them until August 31st. Cheers Hatty! x

Write Harriet's shopping list for a month's supply of pet food. Can she buy it all for under £60?

Running a Car

Q1 Mark's car has to have a full service and MOT this month, and he will have to pay road tax for the year ahead.

Lo-cost Local Garage

Price List:

MOT Test	£55
Interim Service	£65 + VAT
Full Service	£135 + VAT

Summer Special! Have a full service and your MOT with us and get 10% off the total cost.

Urgent Reminder

Ref: MAC19830830

Dear Mr Morrison

Your road tax is due for renewal on 31st August 2010. This will cost £125 for 12 months.
It is now even easier to pay for your road tax online, just go to our website and enter your unique reference number...

a) How much does a **full service** cost, including VAT at 17.5%?

b) How much will it cost to have **both** the service and MOT done with the special offer discount?

c) How much **in total** can Mark expect to spend on his car this month, assuming it needs no repairs?

Q2 Mark is looking for good deals on car insurance for the next year.
His current insurer, Insure-Ants, has offered him a **20% loyalty discount**.
Another company, Chassis-Sure, has offered him a **10% introductory discount**.

www.discombobulated.co.uk

Here are your best 3 quotes:

Win's Wheels	£419
Chassis-Sure	£434
Insure-Ants	£467

Quotes DO NOT include discounts

a) Which is the **cheapest** quote for Mark, taking into account all the discounts?

b) Mark can't afford to pay for the year's insurance in one go, so he pays in monthly instalments which will cost him 7.5% more in total. What is the **lowest amount** he could pay per month?

14

Running a Car

Q3 Sarah is buying a new car. The dealer offers her two payment options:

> Option 1:
> Pay a 20% deposit and then pay the remaining amount in 24 equal monthly payments.

> Option 2:
> Pay no deposit and then 36 monthly payments of £199. After 36 months, the rest must be paid off or the car can be sold back to the garage at its value at that time.

£11 499

a) How much would she have to pay **each month** using Option 1?

b) Sarah decides to pay using Option 2. How much would the **final payment** be?

c) The value of the car falls by **15% each year**. What is its value after 36 months?

Q4 Danni, Darren and Milo share a car to work. Darren doesn't drive, so Danni and Milo take turns. The three of them split the cost of the car share equally. Darren wants to know how much he should be paying the other two each month for fuel.

Both Milo and Danni's cars use on average around 6 litres of fuel per 100 km

Tuesday 11th May

In a typical month, Danni and Milo each drive to work and back **10 times**.

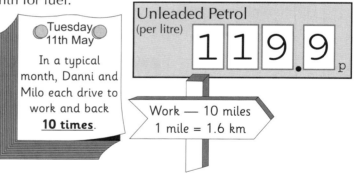

Unleaded Petrol (per litre)

1 1 9 . 9 p

Work — 10 miles
1 mile = 1.6 km

a) How many **km** do they cover **in total** each month to drive to work and back?

b) How much does it cost **in total** for fuel each month to drive to work and back?

c) Darren wants to give each driver an extra **10%** to say thank you for the lifts. How much should he give each driver in total every month, to the nearest 50p?

Running a Car

Q5 Alun's car has failed its MOT. He has been advised to scrap it if the repairs cost more than **two thirds** of its current value. Alun bought his car new for £10 500, 9 years ago, and knows that cars of the same make and model usually decrease in value by around **22% per year**.

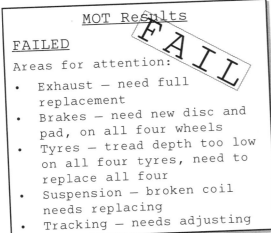

```
        MOT Results
FAILED
Areas for attention:
•  Exhaust — need full
   replacement
•  Brakes — need new disc and
   pad, on all four wheels
•  Tyres — tread depth too low
   on all four tyres, need to
   replace all four
•  Suspension — broken coil
   needs replacing
•  Tracking — needs adjusting
```

Price List
(includes labour costs and VAT)

Tyres			Exhaust	
Each:	£28		Part Replacement:	£140
Pair:	£50		Full Replacement:	£290
Full Set:	£95			
Maintenance			Brakes	
Oil Change:	£49		Pads (each):	£39
Adjust Tracking:	£62		Discs (each):	£59
AirCon Recharge:	£55			
Suspension Coil:	£98			

Should Alun scrap his car or is it worth paying for the repairs?

Q6 Brian has found a used car he likes in the local newspaper, but he thinks the price is too high. He finds a graph showing recent private sales prices for cars of the same age and type.

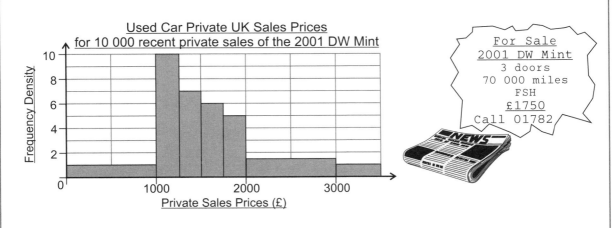

```
For Sale
2001 DW Mint
3 doors
70 000 miles
FSH
£1750
Call 01782
```

The seller argues that it is a fair price because it's the **median value** of the recent private sales. Is he correct?

Running a Car

Q7 Paul's company pays him fuel expenses when he uses his own car for company business. Paul has to submit his own claim forms, so he asks his manager how to work out what he is owed.

> To: <u>Paul</u>
> From: <u>Nia</u>
> Subject: Mileage expenses claims
> _____
>
> Hi Paul,
> I've spoken to HR about your expenses query, and this is what they said:
>
> • For journeys of 30 miles or less, we pay a flat rate of £3.20 plus 16p per mile.
>
> • For journeys over 30 miles, the flat rate is £8 plus 10p for every mile travelled after the first 30 miles (there's no 'per mile' rate for the first 30).
>
> Hope that makes sense, give me a shout if you're still confused.
> Nia

Paul has made two journeys recently which he needs to claim for.
How much should he claim for journeys of length **19** and **42 miles**?

Q8 Paul thinks his company are not paying him enough in fuel expenses for long journeys. He fills up his car with petrol and checks the meter on the dashboard which tells him how many miles he can drive on a full tank, which is **55 litres** according to the manual.

```
07MAY2010  12:04  1743 2

Pump:10 UNLEADED PETROL
53.8 L @ 119.9 pence per L

SUBTOTAL:           £64.51

Paid CARD PAYMENT
    ***********5629

Change:             £0.00
```

For journeys over 30 miles, the flat rate is £8 plus 10p for each mile travelled after the first 30 miles.

What is the **longest journey** Paul can make and still claim enough money to cover his own petrol costs? Give your answer to the nearest whole mile.

Going Out

Q1 Natalie, Claire and Nicky go to a restaurant, known for its alcohol-free cocktails.
The cocktail menu is shown below.

	Glass (275 ml)	Jug (650 ml)	Pitcher (1 l)
Tall Island Boiled Tea	£1.98	£3.90	£6.10
Whoop-whoop!	£1.79	£3.50	£5.55
Marghapolitan	£1.49	£3.05	£4.60

Special Offers!
Happy Hour (7pm-8pm)
10% off all jugs!

a) Natalie thinks they should start off by trying a Whoop-Whoop.
Which **size** should they order to get the best deal?

b) The girls decide to try the Marghapolitan next. Which size is the best value during **Happy Hour**?

c) Their final bill comes to **£18.70**. Natalie and Claire each drank twice as much as Nicky.
If they split the bill **fairly**, how much do they each owe?

Q2 Natalie, Nicky and Claire have been planning a trip to the theme park Frimley Towers.
Tickets usually cost £23.50 each, but the girls have collected discount vouchers, shown below.

Frimley Towers —
Special offer —
1/3 off the price
of one adult ticket.

Frimley Towers — 2 for 1 offer
(Cannot be used in conjunction with any other offers)

Buy 1 ticket
and get 1
HALF PRICE!!

a) Which voucher(s) should the girls use to get the cheapest tickets?

b) Natalie and Claire buy the tickets the cheapest possible way, each paying half.
How much does Nicky owe **each** of the other two for her ticket?

Going Out

Q3 Sarah and Dave Ellingham take their three children Harry, Emily and Goliath to the cinema.
Sarah has **two** vouchers for **15% off** the price of an individual adult ticket.
The children are eligible for child tickets. The prices of tickets and snacks are shown below.

PRICES

Adult:	£6.50
Child:	£4.50
Family Ticket: (2 adults and 2 children)	£20.00

Drink £2.99

Popcorn £2.89

Combo *(1 popcorn and 2 drinks)* £4.10

a) What combination of tickets should the Ellinghams buy to make their trip as cheap as possible?

b) The family want at least **3 drinks** and **3 boxes of popcorn**. What is the cheapest way to buy these?

c) Emily wins a coupon for a **third off** the price of a ticket and goes back to the cinema with Goliath.
What is the **minimum** amount they could spend on tickets and a drink and box of popcorn each?

Q4 Three families, the Lewseys, Cohens and Robinsons go out for a meal together.
There are **3 Lewseys**, **5 Cohens** and **4 Robinsons** at the meal.
At the end of the meal they are given two bills — one for food and one for drinks.

Drinks

2 x white wine (bottle)	£32.00
1 x red wine (glass)	£5.50
2 x beer	£5.20
2 x colas	£2.20
2 x lemonades	£2.20
3 x water	
Total	£47.10

Food

3 x roasts	£25.50
2 x quiche	£10.00
3 x lasagnes	£19.20
3 x duck	£22.50
1 x starfish	£7.50
Total	£84.70

a) The families want to split the food bill according to the **number of people** in each family.
How much does **each family** owe for **food**?

b) The drinks bill is split equally between Mr and Mrs Lewsey, Dr. Robinson,
Mr and Mrs Cohen and Josh Cohen. How much does **each family** owe for **drinks**?

Going Out

Q5 Josh meets up with two other friends, Ben and Jason, for lunch on Tuesday.
From the menu below, Josh and Jason choose **Spaghetti Bolognaise** and Ben chooses **Chilli**.
They share **two garlic breads** and each have **two glasses of orange juice**.

Mains	Sides	Drinks
Cannelloni of the Day (v) £7.50	Chips £2.00	Canned Drinks £1.75
Spaghetti Bolognaise £7.80	Garlic Bread £4.25	Fruit Juices £1.10
Pheasant Stew £4.30	Vegetables £3.50	Mineral Water £1.00
Nachos (v) £6.50		Tea £1.50
Chilli £6.95		Coffee £1.50
Shepherds Pie £6.95		

A 5% charge will be applied to all card transactions.

Disclaimer: All food is eaten at your own risk.

a) Josh has to leave early, before the final bill arrives.
How much should he leave to cover his share, **including** a 10% tip?

b) Jason doesn't have any cash to pay for his share of the bill. A nearby cash machine charges £1.25 for withdrawals. Is it cheaper for him to withdraw money from this machine or pay by card?

Q6 Sarah meets two of her friends, Miriam and Samantha, for drinks.
Sarah has two coffees, Miriam has one coffee and one tea, and Samantha has two teas.
The receipts are shown below.

2 x coffee
1 x tea
Total — £3.90
Your waiter today was Gordon

1 x coffee ☺
2 x tea
Total — £3.75
Your waiter today was Nick

a) How much does a cup of **coffee** cost?

b) How much does **each person** owe?

Old bag!
Has-bean!

Going Out

Q7 Toby has recently moved to a new area and is looking for new activities to do. The local council has information on two activities that Toby is interested in — tennis and live action role-playing (LARPing).

Reddodd Sports Tennis Rackets
Smazenger Pro — £29
Header Techno — £49
Skilson FloTour — £79

Lockwick LARPers

Lockwick LARPers take part in all 15 local LARPing events throughout the year

Whether you're an experienced LARPer or a 1st-timer, come along and give it a go!

Monthly Fees — £9 (1st month free)
Equipment Hire — £14.99 per event or £139 for the year.

Sparkham Tennis Club
New members welcome!

When do we meet? Once a week throughout the year.

How much will it cost me? £120 annual membership, plus £2.50 for each weekly session.

Can I get a discount? Yes, if someone in your family is already a member you'll get a 20% discount on your membership fee.

Any benefits to joining Sparkham? Yes, all members get a 25% discount at Reddodd Sports Shop.

Toby sets himself an **average** budget of £20 per month, and would want this to cover **all** events held by the club, as well as **equipment** costs. Which club, if any, can he afford to join?

Q8 Toby is going for a day trip to the Wild Animal Park in Daleton. He will travel by train from Sparkham, using his Youth Track Card. He budgets no more than £5 to spend on his lunch.

Train Fares (returns)
Lockwick to Sparkham — £5.80
Sparkham to Reddodd — £12.55
Sparkham to Daleton — £15.60

Youth Track Card (Ages 16-25)
Name: Toby Seaborne
This card entitles the holder to 1/3 off all train journeys.
Signature: *T. Seaborne*

Daleton Animal Park — Admission Prices
Full Price — £15
OAPs — £5
Under 10s — free

Special Offer — 30% off entrance price for Daleton Animal Park for all visitors travelling using public transport (valid tickets must be shown)

Toby goes to a cash machine that only dispenses **£10 notes**.
How much money should Toby withdraw to pay for his day out?

Earning and Saving

Q1 Annika is looking in an agency window for a part-time job for her **12-week** summer holidays.
She intends to save **60%** of her weekly wage to put towards going travelling.
She finds these three job adverts:

SUMMERJOBSHOP

Laundry Assistant
12 h per week
£8.50 per hour

SUMMERJOBSHOP

Dog Groomer
16 h per week
£8.25 per hour

SUMMERJOBSHOP

Bricklayer
15 h per week
£8.40 per hour

a) Which of the jobs will pay Annika the **most per week**?

b) What is the most she could have **saved** by the end of the summer?

c) Annika is told that if she earns the equivalent of an annual salary of over **£6475** she will
get tax deducted from her pay. Could she have tax deducted with any of these jobs?

Q2 Willem also plans to go travelling, in **3 years' time**, after university.
He has **£800** to invest in a high interest savings account to save up for his trip.

Sharkley's Building Society

<u>High Interest Account Terms and Conditions:</u>

The annual interest rate will be fixed at <u>**5%**</u> for 3 years.
You will be advised of any changes after this.

Interest on this account will be paid into the account
every 12 months.

No money can be withdrawn without closing the account.

a) How much money will there be in the account after **one year**?

b) Willem thinks he will need **£1000** saved to go travelling.
Will he have enough if he leaves his savings in the account for **three years**?

Earning and Saving

Q3 Gabby has been offered a job selling medical supplies.

> Dear Gabby
>
> We are delighted to offer you the permanent position of **Medical Sales Representative**, with a basic annual salary of **£21 000**, plus monthly commission related to your sales performance:
>
> | Monthly sales: | % of sales paid as commission (on top of basic salary) for that month: |
> |---|---|
> | Less than £10 000 | 0% |
> | £10 000 up to £19 999 | 4% |
> | £20 000 up to £39 999 | 6% |
> | £40 000 and above | 8% |
>
> Your monthly sales target is **£15 000**.

a) What can Gabby expect to earn each month if she is **on target** for sales?

b) Gabby would like to be earning at least **£3000 per month**. How much does she need to make for the company in **monthly sales** in order to earn this?

Q4 **8 years ago**, Gabby put money into the savings bond shown below.
She wants to use this money as a **deposit** to buy a flat.
She has also recorded her monthly earnings over the last year:

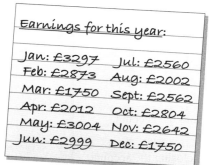

Earnings for this year:

Jan: £3297   Jul: £2560
Feb: £2873   Aug: £2002
Mar: £1750   Sept: £2562
Apr: £2012   Oct: £2804
May: £3004   Nov: £2642
Jun: £2999   Dec: £1750

```
Sharkley's Building Society
        Savings Bond
    (4% interest per year)

Name:        Ms G Gibson
D.O.B.       30 / 08 / 1983
Investment:  £12 000
```

a) The bank will lend Gabby **2.5 times** her annual salary to buy a flat.
How much would this be if she continues to earn the same amount she has done this year?

b) How much money is **currently** in the savings bond?

c) Gabby would need to pay at least **20%** of the value of a flat as a deposit.
What is the most expensive flat she could **currently** afford to buy?

Earning and Saving

Q5 Bob is the union representative for a small company with 15 employees.
He wants to ask the Managing Director, Mr Bigge, to consider a company-wide pay rise.

Annual salaries of the 15 employees

£38 000	£19 000	£20 400
£17 200	£13 400	£14 200
£13 600	£14 200	£17 800
£26 000	£ 11 300	£19 700
£10 200	£11 600	£19 500

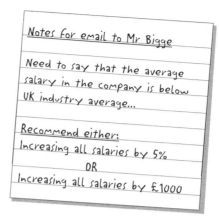

Notes for email to Mr Bigge

Need to say that the average salary in the company is below UK industry average...

Recommend either:
Increasing all salaries by 5%
OR
Increasing all salaries by £1000

a) Which of Bob's suggestions would give the employees the **bigger mean** salary?

b) Which of Bob's suggestions would give the **smallest range** of salaries?

c) Mr Bigge has a budget of **£280 000** to pay the employees next year. What is the **maximum amount** he can increase everyone's salary by? Give your answer to the nearest pound.

Q6 Alice can choose to pay some of her salary into a pension fund each month and her company will also contribute. The fund will pay out when she retires. The options for paying in and paying out are shown below. Alice currently earns **£34 000** per year.

Paying In Options:

Option	% of salary paid by you each month	% of salary paid by company each month
A	4%	4%
B	6%	6%
C	8%	8%

Paying Out Options on Retirement:

Option	How the money will be paid when you retire
X	£4000 lump sum + 15% of final salary every year
Y	£10 000 lump sum + 10% of final salary every year
Z	No lump sum 20% of final salary every year

a) What is the **maximum** amount Alice can expect to be paid into the fund **each year** if she pays no more than £200 a month into her pension fund? She must use one of the three paying in options.

b) Which **paying out** option pays out the most money **in total** if she draws her pension for **20 years**? Assume that Alice's final salary is £34 000.

Earning and Saving

Q7 Pierce had a job for **9 months** on an annual salary of **£12 000**, but his income tax was deducted from his monthly salary assuming he would work for the whole year.
He wants to know how much he can claim back in overpaid taxes at the end of the year.

Working out your Income Tax
A Helpful Guide

Your annual salary is taxed at different rates, as shown:

Salary	Income Tax
up to £6475	0% (Tax Free Allowance)
up to £37 400	20% (on anything above £6475)
£37 401 — £150 000	40% (on anything above £37 400)
over £150 000	50% (on anything above £37 400)

E.g. If you earn £20 000 per year, your monthly tax deduction is 20% of (£20 000 − £6475), split into 12.

a) How much tax did Pierce pay during the **9 months** he was working?

b) How much money can he claim back in overpaid taxes?

Q8 Rich inherits £10 000, and wants to invest it in a high interest account.
He wants to save up to buy a second hand camper van, which will cost about £13 000.

Want to see your money grOW.....?

Either...

Invest in our 5.5% per year 'Fixed Interest Savings Account'.

Just leave your money where it is and the interest rate is guaranteed for 10 yrs.

Interest paid annually.

Or...

Try our new 'Growing Interest Account'.

The interest rate starts at 2% per year, paid annually. The rate then increases by 1% _each year_*, rewarding the long term saver.

*up to 10%.

Which of the two accounts should Rich choose to reach his target in the **shortest time**?

Holidays

Q1 Mrs Thompson is planning a week long holiday in San Foragio, Spain for her husband, son and herself. Their holiday will be in **8 months' time**. Some details are shown below.

> **San Foragio**
> 7 nights, all inclusive — £633 per person
> *20% deposit to be paid at time of booking.*
> *Remaining balance to be paid in monthly installments,*
> *arranged at time of booking.*

> **Car hire (per week)**
> Folkswagon Basic   £70
> Rentault Standard   £80
> Spleurgeot Superior £90
> Posche Luxury   £100

a) How much will Mrs Thompson have to pay as a **deposit** for her family's holiday?

b) Mrs Thompson will pay the remaining balance of the holiday in **eight** equal monthly instalments. How much will she have to pay each month?

c) Mrs Thompson sets aside **£200** per month to pay the monthly instalments **and** to save up for a **hire car** for the week they're away. Which car(s) will she be able to afford to hire?

Q2 Mr Thompson is organising transport to and from the airport, using the information below. It takes **45 mins** to drive to the airport.

> Dear Mrs Thompson,
>
> Booking Ref: 0116573985
> Flight No. Sf098123
> Departure Date: 19/04/10
> Departure Time: 14:35
> Journey Time: 2 hrs 50 mins
>
> Please arrive at least 90 minutes before the scheduled departure time.

Tanner's Travels Travel Company

Destination Information 
Currency:
Euros
Time difference:
1 hour ahead of UK
Climate:
Mediterranean

a) What is the **latest** time the Thompsons can leave home on the day of their departure?

b) Mr Thompson needs to let the car hire company in **Spain** know what time they will arrive at the airport to pick up their car. What is the **earliest** time they will be able to collect their car?

Holidays

Q3   Joe Thompson is unsure what clothes to pack as he doesn't know what the weather will be like in San Foragio in April. He looks up details on the climate in a guidebook:

	Average Temp (°F)	Average Rainfall (mm)	Average Sunshine per day (hrs)
January	52	60	5
February	61	62	5
March	65	67	7
April	77	68	8
May	85	59	10
June	93	48	12

$$°C = (°F - 32) \times \frac{5}{9}$$

a)   What is the average temperature in San Foragio in degrees **Celsius** in April?

b)   From the information in the guidebook, Joe decides that he'll **only** need clothes for warm weather. Is Joe correct to make this assumption?

Q4   Mrs Thompson weighs the family's luggage before they go to the airport. She compares it against the limits set by the airline:

Weight of Bag	0 < kg ≤ 13.5	13.5 < kg ≤ 27.5	27.5 < kg ≤ 36
Excess Charge	None	£42	£75

Joe's luggage   Mr Thompson's luggage   Mrs Thompson's luggage

25 30 35   lbs.

25 30 35   lbs.

25 30 35   lbs.

Unit Conversions
1 kg ≈ 2.2 lbs

a)   How much will the Thompsons have to pay in excess charges?

b)   Suggest how the luggage could be redistributed between the bags so that **no** excess is charged.

Holidays

Q5 The Thompsons are choosing bags to use as **hand luggage** on the plane. They need to make sure that the bags they buy meet the size restrictions set by the airline, shown below.

Ⓐ Volume: 62.4 litres
Height: 42 cm
Length: 55 cm

Ⓑ Volume: 41 litres
Height: 20 cm
Length: 50 cm

Ⓒ Volume: 28 litres
Height: 53 cm
Length: 22 cm

Hand Luggage
Each passesenger is allowed
one piece of hand luggage,
which must not exceed
56 cm x 45 cm x 25 cm.

1 litre = 1000 cm³

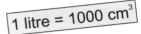

Which bag(s) could the Thompsons use as hand luggage on the plane?

Q6 Joe wants to visit some Roman ruins either with a tour group or by himself. He collects details from the lobby of his hotel, El Hotel, to help him decide which is the best option.

Roman Ruins Day Trip
Departs: 9 am   Returns: 6 pm
Price: €85 (includes all transport, entrance to museum, amphitheatre tour, lunch)
10% discount for El Hotel and Hotel Maris guests.

Local Attractions
Marine World: €9
Roman Museum: €15
Roman Amphitheatre: €10
(Museum and Amphitheatre combined ticket: €20)
Water Splash €12

Bus Timetable

El Hotel	Roman Museum	Amphitheatre
10:30	11:30	11:45
(every hour afterwards until 15:30)		

Amphitheatre	Roman Museum	El Hotel
11:30	11:45	12:45
(every hour afterwards until 16:30)		

All day bus pass — €6

a) Joe thinks he will spend about €10 on lunch. How much would he **save** by going on the trip by himself rather than going on the organised tour?

b) Joe wants to spend at least two and a half hours at the Roman museum and two hours at the amphitheatre. Would he be able to do this if he travelled independently?

Holidays

Q7 Mrs Thompson wants to buy a luxury ham that's a speciality of the region.
She thinks it'll be cheaper to buy it in Spain than at home and compares the price in a shop in San Foragio with the price in the UK.

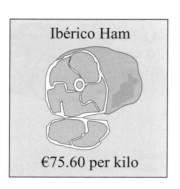

Ibérico Ham

€75.60 per kilo

Things to buy in Spain...
Castanets for Pip
Iberico ham? (£35.20 per lb in UK)
Flamenco shoes (red)

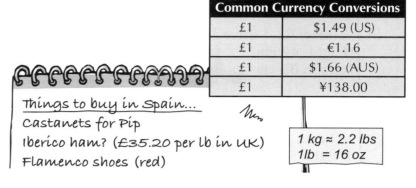

Common Currency Conversions	
£1	$1.49 (US)
£1	€1.16
£1	$1.66 (AUS)
£1	¥138.00

1 kg ≈ 2.2 lbs
1lb = 16 oz

Mrs Thompson wants to buy a 5 lb 4 oz ham. How much would she **save in pounds** by buying the ham in Spain rather than in the UK?

Q8 The Thompsons' hire car is out of fuel. They only want to buy enough to get them back to the airport from their hotel in San Foragio. Mr Thompson uses the information below to work out how much he needs to buy.

At the petrol station...
petrol station — gasolinera
petrol — gasolina
diesel — gasoil
per litre — por litro

Vehicle Information
Registration: _1906 BJK_
Fuel Type: _Petrol_
Fuel Efficiency: _48 miles per gallon_

Travel Car Co.

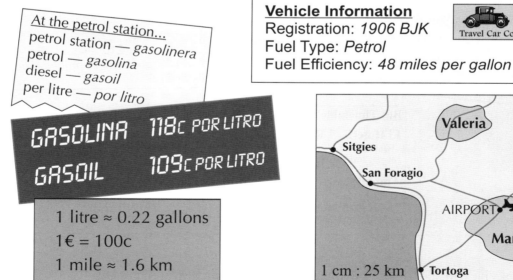

GASOLINA   118c POR LITRO

GASOIL   109c POR LITRO

1 litre ≈ 0.22 gallons
1€ = 100c
1 mile ≈ 1.6 km

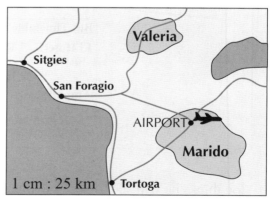

Valeria

Sitgies

San Foragio

AIRPORT

Marido

1 cm : 25 km   Tortoga

Mr Thompson can't speak Spanish so can't tell the attendant how much fuel to put in the car.
He gives him **money** for the amount he wants instead. How much should he give the attendant?

Paying Bills

Q1 Aimee gets her gas and electricity from different suppliers.
Both suppliers charge the same amount per unit, but offer different discounts.

Potteries Power

Dear Ms Morrell

Please find attached your annual statement for gas usage. Last year you spent £186.21 on gas.

We are also able to provide you with electricity, and as a valued customer we can offer you a discount of **7.5%** on next years' electricity bill if you get both your gas and electricity from us...

General Generators

Dear Ms Morrell

Our records show that you spent **£446.72** on electricity last year.

I write to inform you of our unbeatable discounts for using General Generators for your gas as well as your electricity.

Switch today, and we will give you a whopping _17.5% discount_ on your gas bill next year...

---

a) How much could Aimee expect to pay for her **electricity** with Potteries Power?

b) How much could Aimee expect to pay for her **gas** with General Generators?

c) Which supplier should she choose so that she pays the least amount in total?

Q2 Aimee currently lives alone but has asked her friend Emma to move in to help her save money.
She wants Emma to pay £180 for rent, £40 for utilities, plus half the council tax bill, **per month**.

```
            Sinn City Council

        Council Tax Statement

        Occupant:    Ms A Morrell
        Period:      05/2010 - 04/2011
        Discounts:   25% reduction for
                     single occupancy
        Charges:     £973.80

        Status: Paid in full
```

a) With Emma in the flat, Aimee would lose her 'single occupancy' discount.
How much would **next year's** council tax bill cost with two people in the flat?

b) How much should Emma pay Aimee **per month** in total?

Paying Bills

Q3   Dave and Kate live together and split all the household bills. Dave earns more than Kate, so he thinks they should split the bills in **proportion** to how much they each earn.

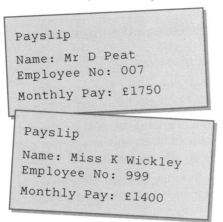

Payslip

Name: Mr D Peat
Employee No: 007
Monthly Pay: £1750

Payslip

Name: Miss K Wickley
Employee No: 999
Monthly Pay: £1400

Monthly Bills:
Rent — £540.00
Gas — £45.00
Electric — £27.45
Water — £20.25
Phone / Internet — £18.90
Council tax — £99.90

a)   How much of **each bill** should Dave and Kate pay?

b)   How much will they each have **left** from their monthly pay, after they have paid the bills?

Q4   Dave and Kate are considering having a water meter installed which they hope will save them money on their water bill. Instead of a fixed monthly charge of £20.25, the bill would depend on the amount of water they used.

Windydale Water

Trying to save money on your bills?
Have one of our water meters installed for
FREE!

Windydale Water

Water Meter Installation
Terms and Conditions

With a Windydale water meter you will pay each month:

* standing charge of £2.70
* £1.25 per m³ of water used

1 m³ = 1000 litres

The average person in the UK uses around **155 litres** of water per day. If Dave and Kate both use this amount, how much could they save **annually** by having a meter installed?

Paying Bills

Paying Bills

Q5 Joe wants to switch to a new mobile phone tariff as he feels he is currently paying too much.

He takes his last bill into a mobile phone shop to get some advice on the best tariff for him.

> Bug-Talk
> Dear Mr King
> Here is a summary of your mobile phone usage for March 2010:
> Calls: 272 mins
> Texts: 374
> Total Cost: £85.96

Tariff	Monthly Fixed Charge	No. of Free Minutes per month	Cost of Calls (per min)	No. of Free Texts per month	Cost of Texts (per text)
Dungbeetle	£10	0	20p	100	12p
Earwig	£15	100	15p	200	10p
Praying Mantis	£25	200	5p	500	10p

17.5% VAT is added to all charges.

a) Which would be the cheapest tariff for Joe to switch to if he sticks with his **current** usage?

b) Joe can get a **10% discount** on his bill by signing up for a longer contract. How much would he have saved on his last bill if he was on the cheapest tariff and had this discount?

Q6 Joe also wants to change his electricity provider.
He has found the following chart on the internet comparing all the major suppliers:

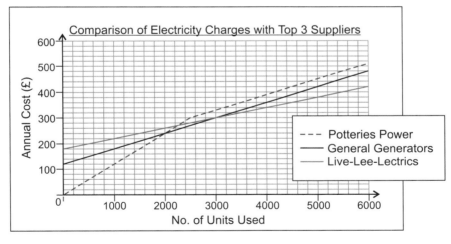

Comparison of Electricity Charges with Top 3 Suppliers

- - - Potteries Power
—— General Generators
—— Live-Lee-Lectrics

(Annual Cost (£) vs No. of Units Used)

a) According to his most recent bill, Joe used **3874 units** of electricity last year.
Which supplier would be cheapest if he uses the same amount of electricity next year?

b) Another smaller supplier charges a fixed amount of **£12.50 per month**, plus **7p per unit**.
For the amount of electricity Joe uses, is it cheaper to use this supplier rather than the others?

Paying Bills

Q7   Five friends are renting a house together.
The total monthly rent is **£1350**, which covers all bills apart from the TV licence and the internet.
The people with big rooms have agreed to pay **1.5 times more rent** than those with small rooms.
The TV licence and internet bills will only be split between the people who use them.

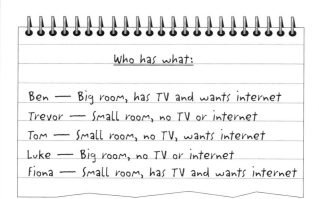

Who has what:

Ben — Big room, has TV and wants internet
Trevor — Small room, no TV or internet
Tom — Small room, no TV, wants internet
Luke — Big room, no TV or internet
Fiona — Small room, has TV and wants internet

TV Licence Fees
Spread the cost of your TV Licence by paying monthly — only £12.20 per month.

Broadbean Broadband Internet
Special Offer!
Sign up now and pay just £14.70 per month!

How much will each of the people in the house have to pay **per month**?

Q8   Cameron is buying a new sofa for **£1500**. The furniture store offers two 'buy now pay later' payment plans which will allow Cameron to start paying for his sofa in 12 month's time:

Plan A	Plan B
For purchases up to £2000, enjoy 3 months interest free, and no repayments for one year.	For purchases up to £3000: 0% interest* for 6 months and no repayments needed for 12 months.
3 months after purchase, compound interest will be charged at a rate of 1.5% per month.	*After 6 months, compound interest will be charged monthly at a rate of 2%.

a)   Which plan will charge Cameron the **least amount of interest** in total over the year?

b)   After 12 months, Cameron wants to pay **60%** of what he owes, then pay the rest **one month later**. What is the lowest amount Cameron will have to repay **in total**?

Decorating

Q1 Lisanna wants to paint three of the walls in her bedroom soft blue.
She has made some notes to help her work out how much paint she needs.

To be painted (drawings not to scale)...

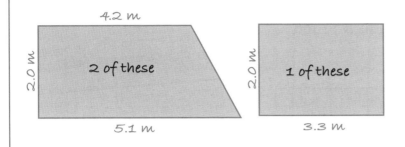

4.2 m

2.0 m

2 of these

5.1 m

2.0 m

1 of these

3.3 m

Soft blue paint...?
Mix white paint and blue paint in the ratio 7 : 2.

1 litre emulsion covers 14 square metres...

Will all need 2 coats though!

a) What is the total area to be painted?

b) How much paint will Lisanna need in total for the three walls?

c) Lisanna finds a 1.2 litre tin of white paint in the shed at home.
How much **more** white paint will she need to buy?

Q2 Zoe is replacing one of her windows with panels of stained glass, as shown.
She has measured the window in millimetres, but the glaziers have asked for measurements in imperial units.

Grandpa Glass
Bespoke Glaziers

Made to measure panes of stained and decorative glass.

Prices vary, but typically 10p per square inch.

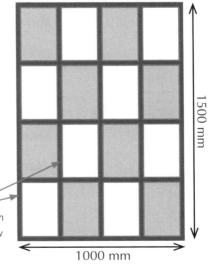

1500 mm

1000 mm

1 inch ≈ 2.5 cm
Give measurements in inches as fractions rather than decimals.

Wooden supports between panes and around window are half an inch wide.

a) What is the height and width of the window in inches?

b) What is the height and width (in inches) of each **individual** pane of glass Zoe needs?

c) Zoe has budgeted £200 to buy the glass for the window. Is this likely to be enough?

Decorating

Q3   Gill runs a small business. She is working out the cost of refurbishing her office space.
A scale plan of the office is shown here.

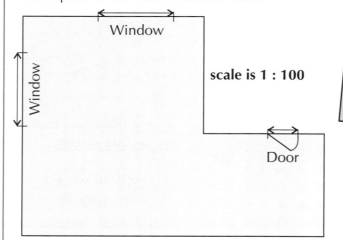

scale is 1 : 100

Office Flooring Megastore
Special Offers!
- Laminate flooring only <u>£5 per m²</u>
- Easy-care carpet now just <u>£8 per m²</u>

Top Quality Skirting Boards
Only <u>£2.75</u> per metre!
(Sold in metre lengths only)

a)   Gill will need skirting boards to go all around the office, except for the doorway.
How much will the new skirting boards cost?

b)   Gill also needs new flooring. How much would she
save by choosing laminate flooring instead of carpet?

Q4   Gill wants to know whether wallpaper or paint would be cheaper for her reception area.
The room is square and measures 3.2 m × 3.2 m, with walls 2.6 m high. There are two
doors, which are 2.1 m high and 0.8 m wide (including frames), and no windows.

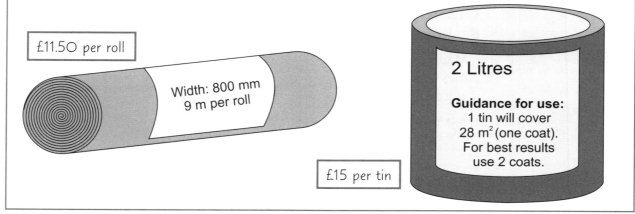

£11.50 per roll

Width: 800 mm
9 m per roll

£15 per tin

2 Litres

Guidance for use:
1 tin will cover
28 m² (one coat).
For best results
use 2 coats.

a)   Calculate the area of the walls to be painted or wallpapered.

b)   Compare the cost of wallpapering the walls with that of painting the walls with two coats.

c)   How much would it cost for Gill to wallpaper **one** of the
walls without a door and paint the others using two coats?

Decorating

Q5   Charlie and Nik have built an extension to their kitchen to be used as a utility room.
Charlie is ordering a new washing machine and tumble drier to be fitted into the room as
shown on the sketch below.

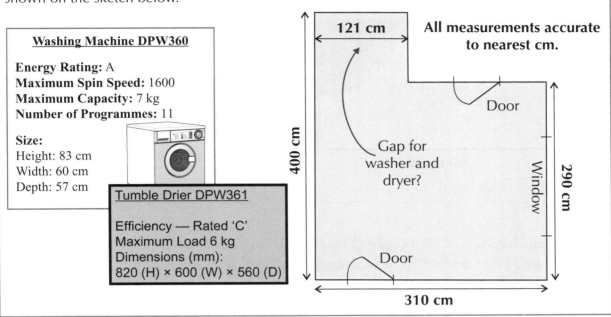

Washing Machine DPW360

Energy Rating: A
Maximum Spin Speed: 1600
Maximum Capacity: 7 kg
Number of Programmes: 11

Size:
Height: 83 cm
Width: 60 cm
Depth: 57 cm

Tumble Drier DPW361

Efficiency — Rated 'C'
Maximum Load 6 kg
Dimensions (mm):
820 (H) × 600 (W) × 560 (D)

121 cm

All measurements accurate
to nearest cm.

Door

400 cm

Gap for
washer and
dryer?

Window

290 cm

Door

310 cm

If the dimensions of the appliances are correct to 2 significant figures, will the
washing machine and tumble drier fit side by side in the gap Charlie has chosen?

Q6   Nik wants to tile one of the walls of the utility room (height 230 cm, width 400 cm).
The tiles and adhesive needed are shown here.

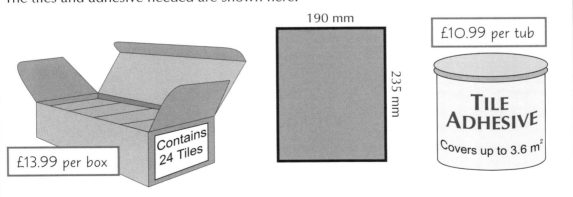

190 mm

£10.99 per tub

235 mm

TILE
ADHESIVE

Covers up to 3.6 m²

Contains
24 Tiles

£13.99 per box

Estimate the cost of tiling the wall.

Decorating

Q7 Colin wants to lay gravel to form a patio and two paths in his garden, as shown below.

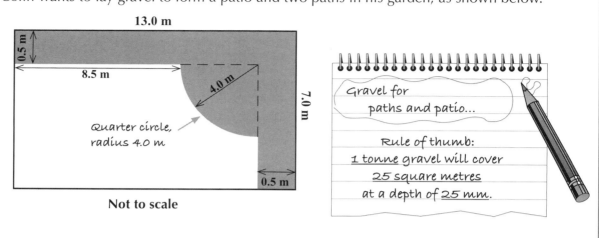

Not to scale

How much gravel will Colin need to buy if the paths and patio are to be 25 mm deep? Give your answer to the nearest 10 kg.

Q8 Colin's friend Geoff is laying a concrete patio. He needs 1500 kg of concrete. He expects the job to take three days in total.

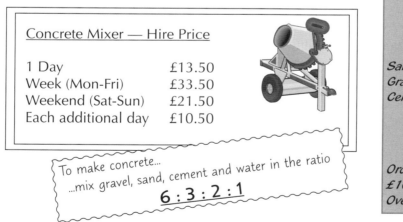

How much will it cost Geoff to lay the patio in the **cheapest** way possible?

Safety and Design

Q1   Hin-Tak is designing some folding boxes to hold a range of books to be delivered by post.

His design involves scoring fold lines on a large sheet of cardboard which allow it to be folded to form a lidless box, as shown:

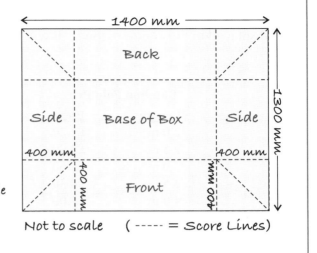

How box should look, and how books should be stacked:

Front

Side

← 1400 mm →

Back

Side   Base of Box   Side

400 mm   400 mm

400 mm   400 mm

Front

Not to scale   (----- = Score Lines)

1300 mm

a)   What will the **dimensions** of the box be?

b)   What will the **volume** of the box be?

c)   Each book is 200 mm high, 150 mm wide and 15 mm thick. What is the largest number of books that will fit in each cardboard box, if they are arranged as shown?

Q2   The boxes of books are weighed before Kim, the delivery driver, loads up his van. Kim has a list of the boxes he needs to deliver:

```
For Delivery:

5 boxes at 14 kg each
40 boxes at 3 kg each
10 boxes at 25 kg each
10 boxes at 12 kg each
3 boxes at 74 kg each
9 boxes at 62 kg each
8 boxes at 79 kg each
```

MAX LOAD = 2000 kg

M107 GVE

The weight of each box is accurate to the nearest kg.
Is it safe for Kim to load all of the boxes onto his van?

Safety and Design

Q3 To commemorate the centenary of her town, Constantina is making a flag to be displayed in the centre of town. It will be mounted on a bamboo frame, as shown:

Bamboo Pole Prices

Length	Price
2.0 m	£2.20
2.5 m	£2.90
3.0 m	£3.60
3.5 m	£4.30
4.0 m	£5.00

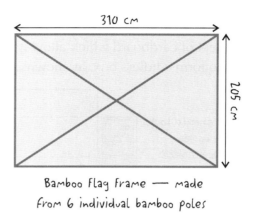

310 cm

205 cm

Bamboo flag frame — made from 6 individual bamboo poles

a) What is the length of each **diagonal** bamboo frame pole, to the nearest cm?

b) Each of the six frame poles needs to be cut to size from a longer pole.
What is the **lowest total cost** of the bamboo poles?

Q4 Constantina is also making a flag to completely cover one of the outside walls of the town hall.

To work out the height of the building, she stands 5 m away from the wall and measures the **angle of elevation** from the ground to the top of the wall, as shown:

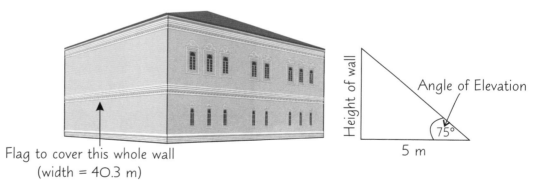

Flag to cover this whole wall
(width = 40.3 m)

Height of wall

Angle of Elevation

75°

5 m

a) How **tall** is the town hall, to the nearest 10 cm?

b) She wants to make the flag by stitching together 100 small pieces of cloth in a 10 by 10 arrangement. What **area** of cloth is needed for each piece, in m² to 1 d.p.?

Safety and Design

Q5 Jimmy is making a wooden DVD storage unit, as shown here:

He wants to make space for **100 DVDs**, and has measured a standard DVD box to work out the dimensions required.

DVD Box Dimensions:

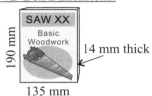

190 mm
135 mm
14 mm thick
SAW XX
Basic Woodwork

Front View of DVD Unit:

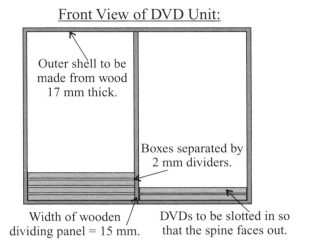

Outer shell to be made from wood 17 mm thick.

Boxes separated by 2 mm dividers.

Width of wooden dividing panel = 15 mm.

DVDs to be slotted in so that the spine faces out.

a) Jimmy's measurements of the DVD box are accurate to the nearest mm. What are the **maximum** dimensions of each DVD box?

b) The measurements of the wood and dividers for the unit are also accurate to the nearest mm. What should the **outer dimensions** be for the unit to ensure the DVDs will fit as planned?

Q6 Sam is designing a removable wooden wheelchair ramp for the front door of his grandad's house. He has researched the relevant safety advice and sketched out a design.

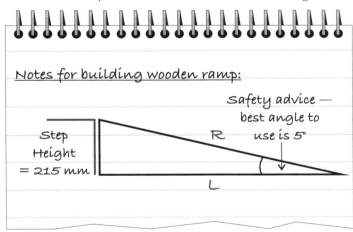

Notes for building wooden ramp:

Safety advice —
best angle to
use is 5°

Step Height
= 215 mm

R

L

a) What will be the **lengths** of L and R, to the nearest cm, if Sam follows the safety advice?

b) Sam orders wooden planks of length **2.5 m**, accurate to the nearest **10 cm**. Can he be sure that this will be big enough for the longest length of wood required?

Safety and Design

Q7 A new art gallery is being designed with a sloping roof made entirely of solar panels, as shown in the sketch here:

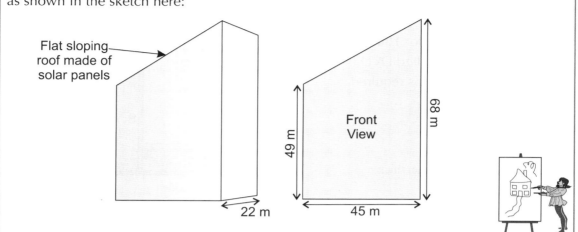

Flat sloping roof made of solar panels

49 m

68 m

Front View

22 m

45 m

a) What **area** of solar panels will be required for the roof of the building? Give your answer to the nearest m².

b) The company making the solar panels need to know the **angle** between the sloping roof and the horizontal to the nearest degree. What should the designers tell them?

Q8 Li is designing a cardboard scale model of the planned gallery to post out to interested artists. The model will be cut out as a net from A4 card to be posted out flat then folded up to display.

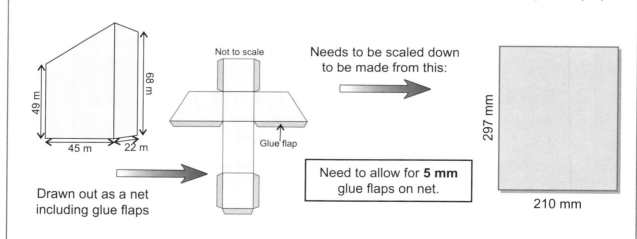

49 m

68 m

45 m

22 m

Drawn out as a net including glue flaps

Not to scale

Glue flap

Needs to be scaled down to be made from this:

Need to allow for **5 mm** glue flaps on net.

297 mm

210 mm

Li wants to use a scale of **1 : 800** for the model. Work out if he will be able to cut the net from **one piece** of A4 card using this scale.

Environmental Issues

Q1 For his biology coursework Mubasher is investigating the size of frogs in the school pond. He collects the data shown below.

> Lengths of frogs: 3.5 cm 4.7 cm 7.1 cm 3.6 cm 2.4 cm 3.8 cm
> 6.4 cm 4.0 cm 5.7 cm 6.9 cm 5.3 cm 2.6 cm 4.9 cm 5.8 cm

a) What is the **mean** length of the frogs in the pond? Give your answer to 3 s.f.

b) What is the **range** of lengths of the frogs in the pond?

Q2 Melissa uses oil to heat her home. She wants to reduce the amount of oil she uses. On September 1st 2010 she looks at how much oil she has left and how much she bought in the last 12 months.

Volume:
2000 litres

Empty   Full

Account holder: Melissa Gordon			
	Debit	Credit	Balance
12/03/10 West County Oil	£465		£1250.78

September 1st 2009
West County Oil
2000 litres delivered
Total Price: £1096

a) How much oil is left in Melissa's oil tank?

b) Assuming the price of oil **didn't change** between September 2009 and March 2010, calculate the volume of oil that was delivered in **March**.

c) How much oil does Melissa use each month, on **average**?

Environmental Issues

Q3 The head teacher of Greenodd High School asks the Student Council to carry out a project to investigate littering in the school grounds. They start by designing a questionnaire about why pupils drop litter. Part of the Student Council's questionnaire is shown below.

> Q3 Do you drop litter a lot?
>   Yes ☐   No ☐
>
> Q4 Why do you drop litter?
>   Laziness ☐   To look cool ☐   There aren't enough bins ☐
>
> Q5 What would make you stop dropping litter?
>   More bins ☐   Punishments for littering ☐   Nothing ☐

a) Give **three criticisms** of the questionnaire designed by the student council.

b) Suggest a better question that could be used instead of question 3.

c) Suggest a suitable way for the questionnaire to be **distributed** and explain your reasoning.

Q4 The Student Council also did a 'litter count' around the school grounds. They have to analyse the results, some of which are shown below, and present them to the head teacher.

Table showing the different types of litter found in different areas of the school:

Area:	Food Wrappers	Bottles	Cans	Other
Yard	ЖТ ЖТ ЖТ ІІ	ЖТ ІІІ	ІІІ	ЖТ ЖТ
Field	ЖТ ЖТ ІІІ	ЖТ	І	ЖТ ІІ
Library	ЖТ І	ЖТ ІІ	ІІ	ЖТ І
Grassed Area	ЖТ ЖТ І	ІІІ	ЖТ І	ЖТ ІІ

Draw a suitable chart showing the **proportions** of the different **types** of litter found in and around the school.

Environmental Issues

Q5 Iain is analysing recycling data for the council. He's been asked to look at the amount of waste that households in an area **recycle** per week compared to the amount that is sent to **landfill**.

Mass of rubbish recycled (kg)	0 ≤ m < 3	3 ≤ m < 6	6 ≤ m < 9	9 ≤ m < 12	12 ≤ m < 15
Number of households	29	34	36	31	18

Mass of rubbish sent to landfill (kg)	0 ≤ m < 5	5 ≤ m < 10	10 ≤ m < 15	15 ≤ m < 20	20 ≤ m < 25
Number of households	9	17	36	52	34

a) Compare the **mean** amount of rubbish recycled per household with the **mean** amount per household sent to landfill.

b) Estimate what **percentage** of the total amount of rubbish produced each week is recycled.

Q6 Carl wants to work out how fuel efficient his car is. He fills his petrol tank up and records the number of miles the car has done. When he gets to a petrol station, Gulfaco, he refills the tank and again checks the mileometer.

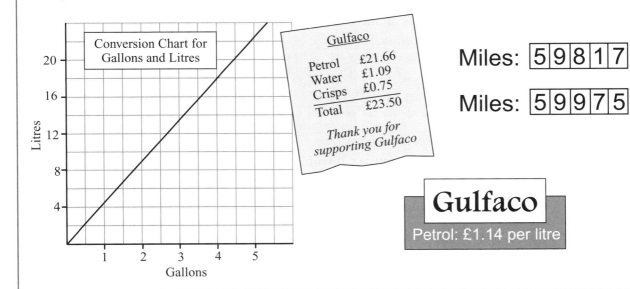

Calculate the **efficiency** of Carl's car in miles per gallon.

Health and Fitness

Q1 Anna runs a monthly competition for her circuit training class at Udderston Leisure Centre. Each class member has to do as many repetitions as they can in a minute on each activity. The winner is the person with the **highest mean score**. This month's scores are shown below:

Member	Press-ups	Sit-ups	Chin-ups	Dips	Squats
Asif	18	39	12	31	42
Brad	24	29	14	24	38
Christian	31	43	19	18	61
Declan	34	38	21	35	55
Ezra	26	49	8	25	60
Fintan	12	56	14	18	48
George	19	24	18	21	37
Hermez	32	30	22	19	50

a) Who won this month's competition?

b) Anna is thinking of reducing the time allowance for the **highest mean scoring** activity. Which one would you recommend changing?

c) She also wants to change the activity with the **least consistent scoring**. Which activity is this?

Q2 Anna also wants to make some changes to her weekly circuit training class.

She has written the following questionnaire to give to her members.

She hopes it will help her decide which activity to take out, and what to replace it with.

> Circuit Training Class Questionnaire
>
> 1. Do you like my circuit training classes?
>   ☐ yes ☐ no
>
> 2. Which activity do you dislike?
>   ....
>
> 3. Do you agree that I should replace one of the activities with **skipping**?
>   ☐ yes ☐ no
>
> Thank you for filling out this questionnaire. Please write your name on the top and hand it back to me at the end of the class.

a) Suggest **three reasons** why Anna may not get reliable results from the questionnaire.

b) Re-write each of Anna's questions to help her get more reliable results.

Health and Fitness

Q3 Marcus is on a calorie controlled diet to try to lose weight. To maintain his current weight he needs a daily calorie intake of **2500**, so he is aiming to reduce his intake to an average of **1800** calories a day. He has been keeping a food diary to monitor his daily calorie intake.

Marcus' Food Diary

Monday
Good start— 1700

Tuesday
Not bad — 1850

Wednesday
Oops — 2000

Thursday
Better — 1800

Friday
Still ok — 1850

Saturday
Oh dear — 2400

Sunday
Good — 1700

Weighty Issues!

...For every 3500 calories under your normal* calorie intake you can expect to lose 1 lb in weight...

*normal calorie intake means the amount needed to maintain your current weight.

a) Did Marcus meet his target for average daily calorie intake this week?

b) How much weight could Marcus expect to lose each week at his **current** calorie intake?

Q4 Dominic is training for a triathlon.
His coach, Paul, has sent him a training schedule in the form of a graph.

Hi Dom
Starting this weekend I want you to match the pace on this graph with a swim, a cycle and a run. It's shorter than the actual race but it will help you work up to the right pace. I've allowed for time to get changed in between each part. See you soon, Paul.

The actual race is a 1 km swim, followed by a 20 km cycle ride, and then a 5 km run.

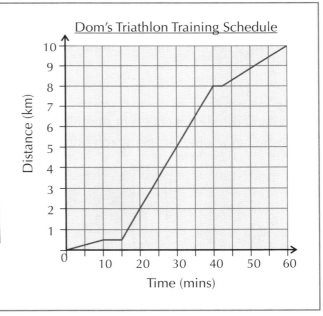

Dom's Triathlon Training Schedule

a) Describe in as much detail as possible what Paul expects Dominic to do during training, including the **target average speeds** (in km/h) for each section.

b) In a training session, Dominic sets out at 10.15 for the swim and gets off his bike at 11.03. If he can change in 2 minutes, how long will he have left to complete the run in his **target time**?

c) In the week before the race, Dominic can complete each section at the target pace set by Paul. **How long** should he take to finish the triathlon assuming he can maintain this pace?

Health and Fitness

Q5 Cassie runs a slimming club. To have a visual representation of the heights and weights of new members, she plots them as a scatter graph, as shown below.

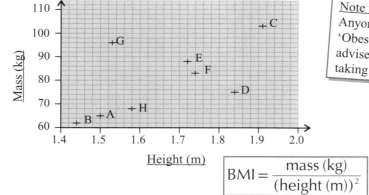

Note to all new members:
Anyone who can be described as 'Obese' by Body Mass Index (BMI) is advised to seek medical advice before taking part in the classes

$$BMI = \frac{mass\ (kg)}{(height\ (m))^2}$$

Body Mass Index Ranges

Below 18.5 — Underweight
18.5 to 24.9 — Healthy
25 to 30 — Overweight
Above 30 — Obese

a) Based on the scatter graph, identify **one** member that may need to seek medical advice before taking part in the classes.

b) Calculate the BMI of this member to see if your prediction was correct.

c) Identify a member who may **not** need to lose weight, and calculate their BMI to check.

Q6 To demonstrate the effects of slimming club attendance on Body Mass Index, Cassie has another scatter graph from a study of 15 previous members of her club.

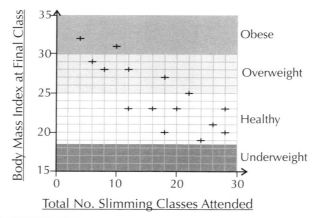

a) What does Cassie's scatter graph suggest about the effect of her classes on Body Mass Index?

b) Use the chart to recommend a **minimum** number of classes needed for a healthy BMI.

Health and Fitness

Q7 Cassie wants to write a press release to advertise the success of her slimming club.
She has records of the start and end weights of previous members who stayed for 3 months.

Start Weight (w kg)	$80 \leq w < 90$	$90 \leq w < 100$	$100 \leq w < 110$	$110 \leq w < 120$	$120 \leq w < 130$
No. of people	4	7	11	5	3

End Weight (w kg)	$70 \leq w < 80$	$80 \leq w < 90$	$90 \leq w < 100$	$100 \leq w < 110$	$110 \leq w < 120$
No. of people	2	11	8	5	4

Estimate the **mean** start and end weights of the previous members, and use this
to write a statement for Cassie's press release about the success of the club.

Q8 Chris is the manager of Udderston Leisure Centre. She has received complaints from
members about the availability of the exercise bikes and treadmills, and is considering
enforcing a time limit on the machines. She has monitored their use over a typical day.

Time Spent on Exercise Bike (t mins)	Frequency
$0 < t < 5$	10
$5 \leq t < 10$	21
$10 \leq t < 15$	19
$15 \leq t < 20$	18
$20 \leq t < 25$	7
$25 \leq t < 30$	3
$30 \leq t < 35$	2

Time Spent on Treadmill (t mins)	Frequency
$0 < t < 5$	11
$5 \leq t < 10$	16
$10 \leq t < 15$	13
$15 \leq t < 20$	15
$20 \leq t < 25$	12
$25 \leq t < 30$	8
$30 \leq t < 35$	5

a) Find the average (**median**) time users spent on each of the machines.

b) Chris wants to set the time limits so that only **10%** of members have to reduce their
time on each machine. Suggest time limits for both the bike and the treadmill.

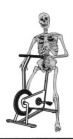

Running a Business

Q1 Ali runs a sock company, and has been asked to present some sales data at a seminar.
She wants to present it as a graph to make it easier to spot trends in the data.

From: Jai
To: Ali
Subject: June's Sales
_____

Hi Ali
Just working out the figures for June.
Looks like we're down by 20% on May's sales!
Good luck at the seminar.
Jai.

Month	Sales (£1000s)
January	51
February	39
March	32
April	26
May	20

a) Draw a **suitable graph** for Ali to present the sales data from January to June.

b) Suggest **two statements** Ali could make to summarise the trend in the sales.

c) Predict the sales for **July** if they continue the change from May to June.

Q2 Ali also has to discuss the difference in sales of socks in two of her shops. Each shop's manager
has sent her a breakdown of the number of pairs sold each day, over the same number of days.

Suki's Sock Sales:

Pairs of Socks Sold Daily	Frequency
0 – 9	18
10 – 19	76
20 – 29	52
30 – 39	22
40 – 49	12

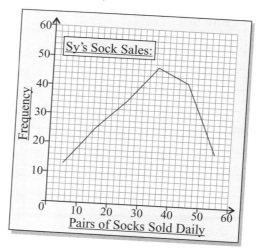

a) Find the **median** and **modal group** for sock sales in both shops.

b) Which shop would you expect to have had the **highest sales** in total? Explain why.

c) How do the two shops compare in terms of **consistency** of sock sales?

Running a Business

Q3   Glenn is starting a business selling vegan chocolate.
He has drawn up a revenue graph for the manufacture of his chocolate.

He spent **£400** initially on the equipment and marketing.

He expects to sell **200 bars** each week.

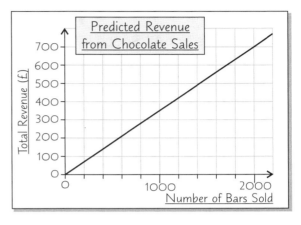

a)   How many **full weeks** will it take Glenn to make back the money he spent on equipment and marketing?

b)   What will be Glenn's total revenue in **one year**, if he maintains sales of 200 bars per week?

Q4   As part of his market research, Glenn carried out a survey to find out who was most likely to buy his chocolate. The results are shown below:

Age Group	No. of people asked	No. who would buy the chocolate
0 – 19	11	3
20 – 39	23	15
40 – 59	46	22
60 – 79	12	4
80+	8	3

a)   Glenn wants to focus his marketing on the age group **most likely** to buy the chocolate. Which age group is this?

b)   Glenn gives out free samples to **350 people** in his target age group. How many of these people are likely to buy chocolate from him?

Running a Business

Q5 Amir runs a shop which is part of a chain.
He is looking at the sales data from the last 6 months:

Total Sales For All Shops in Chain

Quarter:	Month:	Sales:
Q1	M1	£70 000
	M2	£80 500
	M3	£92 600
Q2	M4	£106 500
	M5	£122 500
	M6	£140 900

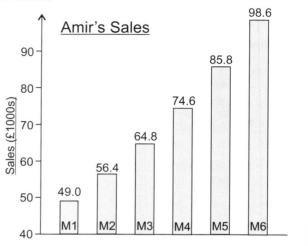

a) Predict the **total sales** for Q3 for all the shops in the chain, based on the percentage change over the last 6 months. Give your answer to the nearest £100.

b) Based on Amir's sales **relative to the total**, estimate his shop's sales for Q3 to the nearest £100.

Q6 A toy company has received an order for an additional **550 000** toy trucks.
The graph below shows the production levels of trucks for the last 50 days.

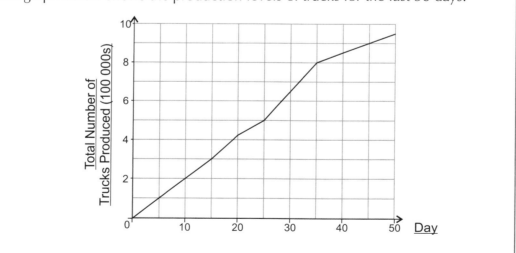

a) What is the average rate of production over the last 50 days?

b) The manager wants to get the order completed quickly, by working at the **highest** production rate from the last 50 days. How many days should the order take to complete at this rate?

Running a Business

Q7 Dhruv is a window cleaner and is looking to increase his business.

He sees an advert for a company that prints leaflets, and orders **1500** leaflets from them:

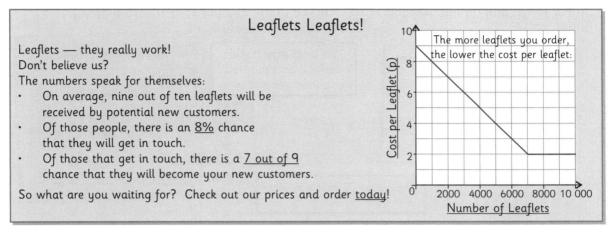

Leaflets Leaflets!

Leaflets — they really work!
Don't believe us?
The numbers speak for themselves:

- On average, nine out of ten leaflets will be received by potential new customers.
- Of those people, there is an <u>8%</u> chance that they will get in touch.
- Of those that get in touch, there is a <u>7 out of 9</u> chance that they will become your new customers.

So what are you waiting for? Check out our prices and order <u>today</u>!

Each new customer earns Dhruv around **£235** per year. How much extra income can he expect to make this year as a result of delivering the leaflets, allowing for the cost of printing?

Q8 Dhruv is making some notes about his expected earnings from his window-cleaning business for next year. He has made some estimates of his expected income and outgoings:

No. of customers: 135
No. of working weeks: 48

Income:
- Payment from customers (£6.40 per week each)
- 20% tip (of weekly amount) from each customer at New Year

Outgoings:
- 20% tax on earnings between £6475 and £37 400
- 40% tax on earnings between £37 401 and £150 000
- Weekly expenses of £65 per week
- Occasional equipment or advertising costs — allow £300 per year

Income tax is worked out **after** all Dhruv's other outgoings have been deducted.
How much money can Dhruv expect to make next year after paying tax?

Hospitals and Healthcare

Q1   Julian is a manager for Trundle Hospital Trust.
He is responsible for ordering pre-made meals for the patients at the hospital.
For lunch **and** dinner, patients have a choice of meal options, as shown below.

Trundle Hospital Trust
Meal Card
Please select from:
☐ Standard
☐ Vegetarian
☐ Low Fat

The probability that a patient is on a restricted low fat diet is 17%

Trundle Hospital Trust

1300 Beds
Typical Daily Occupancy = 84%

The probability that a patient is a vegetarian is 9%

a)   What is the minimum number of **vegetarian** meals Julian should order per day?

b)   What is the minimum number of **low fat** meals Julian should order per day?

c)   Julian is concerned that there is no option for vegetarians on a low fat diet.
How many patients would this apply to on a typical day?

Q2   Julian has noticed that there does not seem to be enough low fat meals on some days.

He decides to monitor the situation to see how many people are needing low fat meals.

Each day for a week, he takes a different random sample of **100 patients** and checks how many of them are on low fat diets.

Day	No. of patients on low fat diets (out of 100 sampled)
Monday	17
Tuesday	19
Wednesday	8
Thursday	32
Friday	15
Saturday	9
Sunday	20

a)   Use Julian's data to estimate the probability that **any one** patient will need a low fat meal.

b)   What could he do to find a **better estimate** for the probability of a patient wanting a low fat meal?

Hospitals and Healthcare

Q3 Emma is a senior nurse in an intensive care ward. The risk of infection is high on the ward. Emma has been asked to report on the effectiveness of a new handwash for staff and visitors in reducing the number of infections on the ward.

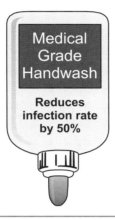

Medical Grade Handwash

Reduces infection rate by 50%

Infection rate on the Intensive Care Ward since the introduction of the Handwash

No. of new infections in one week	No. of weeks.
0	1
1	2
2	7
3	5
4	3
5	2

a) Before the introduction of the handwash, the mean number of new infections per week on Emma's ward was **4**. Is the handwash as effective as the makers claim?

b) Given that on average there are **16 patients** in the ward at any time, what is the probability of a patient catching an infection since the introduction of the handwash?

Q4 Hugh works in a genetic screening clinic. He screens couples who want to start a family to see if they are carriers of a particular genetic disease. Carriers of this disease will not suffer from it, but there is a chance that their baby may be born with it.

Parent 1	Parent 2	Chance of Baby being a Sufferer
Clear	Clear	0
Clear	Carrier	0
Carrier	Carrier	25%
Clear	Sufferer	0
Carrier	Sufferer	50%

Chances of an unaffected person being a carrier: $\frac{1}{30}$

A clear screening reduces the chance of that person being a carrier to **1 in 300**.

a) A couple who **don't** suffer from the disease (but may be carriers) ask Hugh about their chances of having a baby who **does** suffer from it. What should Hugh tell them?

b) Hugh screens the couple and **does not** find them to be carriers. What should he tell them now about the chances of having a baby that suffers from the disease?

Hospitals and Healthcare

Q5 Trundle Hospital Trust have an initiative to reduce waiting times for operations to **18 weeks**. Their targets, and the results from the first two years of the initiative, are shown below.

Trundle Hospital Trust
'Waiting for Operations' Initiative

Our aim is to <u>reduce waiting times</u> for operations so that after 3 years <u>100% of patients</u> wait <u>no longer than 18 weeks</u> for an operation.

We aim to do this as follows:

- **Year 1** — at least **90%** of patients wait 18 weeks or less.
- **Year 2** — at least **95%** of patients wait 18 weeks or less.
- **Year 3** — at least **98%** of patients wait 18 weeks or less.

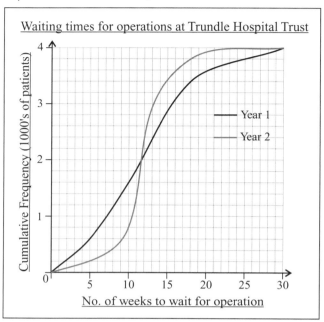

a) What is the **minimum number** of patients that the hospital needs to have waiting 18 weeks or less in Year 3 to remain on target?

b) Can the hospital claim in their annual report to have met their targets in the first two years of the initiative?

Q6 The managers at Trundle Accident and Emergency have targets to improve patients' waiting times:

'The median waiting time should be no more than 20 minutes.'

Waiting Time Targets
In order to improve patients' waiting times at Trundle A&E, we aim to meet targets for average waiting time, and consistency, within the year:
The median waiting time should be no more than 20 minutes. There should be no more than 20 minutes difference in the middle 50% of waiting times.

'There should be no more than 20 minutes difference in the middle 50% of waiting times.'

Sal is doing work experience at the hospital and has been asked to collect data to see if they are meeting their targets. Sal records the waiting times for 120 A&E patients over one week.

Time taken to be assessed (*t* mins)	$0 \leq t < 10$	$10 \leq t < 20$	$20 \leq t < 30$	$30 \leq t < 40$	$40 \leq t < 50$	$50 \leq t < 60$	$60 \leq t < 120$
Frequency	10	46	22	19	15	4	4

Is the department meeting its targets for waiting times?

Local Council Issues

Q1 Sam has been asked by her local council to research how best to use an empty building in town. She first looks at the age of the town residents, as shown below.

Age Of Resident	Frequency
4 and under	622
5-15	953
16-24	2342
25-44	4073
45-64	1167
65-74	962
75 and over	831

Possible options for the building:
• council-run crèche
• a pensioners' day centre
• centre for evening classes aimed at working adults.

a) What percentage of the town are: i) 65 or over ii) 25 - 64   iii) under 5?

b) Which age range contains the **median** age of the town residents?

c) Which of the three options should Sam recommend to the council?

Q2 Kay needs to write a short questionnaire to give out to a sample of residents in the town.

She hopes the results of the questionnaire will help the town library appeal to a wider range of residents.

She has made some notes to help her design the survey.

— Need to find out how often people of different age groups visit the library.

— Need to ask a representative sample of the town!

— How can I make sure people complete the questionnaire?

a) Design **two questions** for the questionnaire, with appropriate option boxes, that will give Kay the best chance of finding out the information she needs.

b) How could Kay choose a **representative** sample of residents to complete the questionnaire?

c) What could she do to make sure that as many people as possible complete the questionnaire?

Local Council Issues

Q3 In January 2010, Bromptown Council installed speed cameras on Bromptown's main road. Trevor is campaigning to have them removed. Both he and the Council have been using the following data to support their views on the effectiveness of the cameras in reducing accidents:

Number of accidents on Bromptown's main road in 2009:

Month	J	F	M	A	M	J	J	A	S	O	N	D
Number of Accidents	7	3	6	1	1	6	2	12	6	3	6	7

Number of accidents on Bromptown's main road in 2010:

Month	J	F	M	A	M	J	J	A	S	O	N	D
Number of Accidents	1	3	2	3	6	2	9	13	5	3	7	12

'Speed Cameras Work'

Bromptown's Councillor Roberts has claimed that the controversial speed cameras on the main road have <u>halved</u> the number of accidents per month.

"In 2009 there was an average of **6 accidents per month**, but our speed cameras have reduced this to an average of **3 per month** in 2010", he said yesterday.

a) Trevor claims the **mean** number of accidents has actually **increased** since the cameras were installed. Is he correct?

b) How can Bromptown Council justify their claim?

Q4 Trevor has asked a sample of Bromptown residents their opinion on the speed cameras so that he can further back up his complaint to the council. His results are shown below:

How do you feel about removing the new speed cameras on the main road?

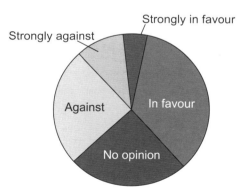

a) What **percentage** of residents surveyed support Trevor's campaign to have the cameras removed?

b) How could these results be used to argue that most residents **don't** want the cameras removed?

Local Council Issues

Q5 Zephyrdale Council are planning to build a wind turbine to provide power to two local schools. Nilesh is a planner in charge of locating the turbine. He is using the diagram below to help him.

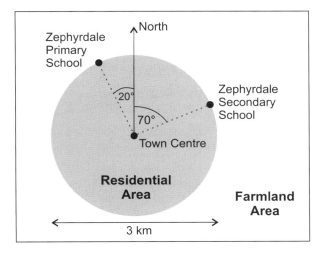

To: Nilesh@ZephyrdaleCouncil.gov.uk
From: Mike@ZephyrdaleCouncil.gov.uk
Subject: Location of Turbine

Hi Nilesh
Could you please draw me up a scale plan of Zephyrdale showing the best place to put the turbine (i.e. halfway between the two schools, and 2 km from the town centre).
Scale of 2 cm : 1 km should be fine.
I want to take it with me to the meeting later.
Thanks
Mike

a) Draw a **scale plan** of Zephyrdale showing the **two potential locations** for the turbine.

b) Mike is told that the plans have changed. The turbine can now go anywhere that's at least **1 km** away from either school, and between **2-3 km** from the town centre. Show this area on a plan.

Q6 Zephyrdale Council decide to invite a representative sample of **20 members** of the Zephyrdale Residents' Association to a meeting to discuss the turbine plans. They find the following table in the Residents' Association annual report:

Zephyrdale Residents' Association
Age and Gender of Members

Age	Male	Female
16-24	21	12
25-44	30	41
45-64	47	31
65+	24	44

Work out how many people of each age group and gender should be invited to the meeting to ensure they get a **representative** sample of the Residents' Association.

Local Council Issues

Q7 Bobenshire County Council plan to **increase** spending on the Police Authority by **3%** for 2011, but keep the amount spent on everything else the **same as in 2010**. Seb is working out how much extra the council will need to charge in council tax to fund this increase in spending.

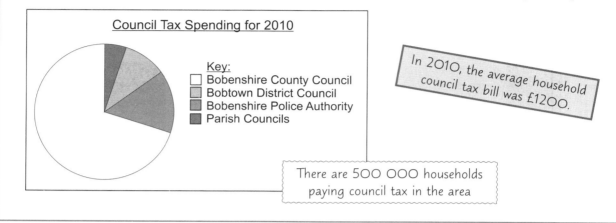

Council Tax Spending for 2010

Key:
- ☐ Bobenshire County Council
- Bobtown District Council
- Bobenshire Police Authority
- Parish Councils

In 2010, the average household council tax bill was £1200.

There are 500 000 households paying council tax in the area

a) By what **percentage** will the council have to increase council tax bills for 2011?

b) Seb claims that this will only increase the average bill by around **£5**. Is he right?

Q8 Trundle District Council recently widened the main road between Udderston and Trundle to try and reduce rush hour traffic congestion. They keep records of the time it takes each morning to get from Udderston to Trundle on the main road, as shown below.

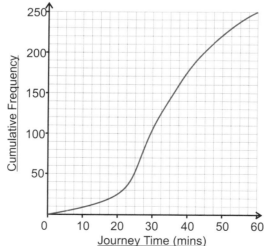

Weekday Rush Hour Journey Times Before Road Widening

Weekday Rush Hour Journey Times
(Data collected for 10 weeks following road widening)

Journey Time (t mins)	No. of Mornings
$0 < t < 20$	7
$20 \leq t < 25$	15
$25 \leq t < 30$	14
$30 \leq t < 35$	9
$35 \leq t < 45$	4
$45 \leq t < 60$	1

The council claims the data shows that the money spent on the road is justified. Are they right? Explain your answer.

Chickens Crossing

Science in the Workplace

Q1 Soraya works in a hospital lab preparing tissue samples taken from patients.
Each sample must be no more than **five cells thick**.
Soraya measures the thickness using this detector:

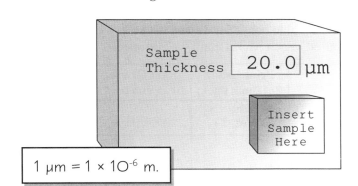

Sample Thickness 20.0 μm

Insert Sample Here

$1 \, \mu m = 1 \times 10^{-6} \, m.$

a) Soraya knows that each of these cells is around 0.000004 m thick. What is this in **μm**?

b) Is the sample on the detector the correct thickness?

c) Soraya is asked to prepare a different sample using cells which are 0.0000015 m thick.
What is the **maximum reading** the detector should display for this sample?

Q2 Soraya has been asked to prepare some bacteria samples for the research lab.
The bacteria **double** in number **every hour**.

From: <u>Tina</u>
To: <u>Soraya</u>
Subject: Urgent! — Bacteria Samples

Hi Soraya
Tina here, from the research lab. Could you please get
a bacteria sample across to us by the time we get back
from lunch at 1 pm?
We need at least 1×10^{12} bacteria.
Many thanks,
Tina.

8 a.m. —
1×10^{10} bacteria

a) Will Soraya have a large enough sample by **1 pm**?

b) She needs to split the large sample of 1×10^{12} into **ten** equal smaller samples.
How many bacteria should be in each sample?

Science in the Workplace

Q3 Arthur runs a factory which makes small batches of paper to order.
One order is shown below:

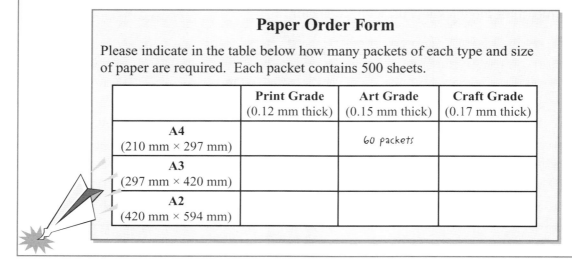

Paper Order Form

Please indicate in the table below how many packets of each type and size of paper are required. Each packet contains 500 sheets.

	Print Grade (0.12 mm thick)	Art Grade (0.15 mm thick)	Craft Grade (0.17 mm thick)
A4 (210 mm × 297 mm)		60 packets	
A3 (297 mm × 420 mm)			
A2 (420 mm × 594 mm)			

a) What **volume** of paper does Arthur need to make for this order? Give your answer in m³ to 3 s.f.

b) Arthur needs **667 kg** of mixed pulp to make **each m³** of this paper. **80%** of the pulp should be from recycled stock. How much recycled pulp will he need to make this batch?

Q4 To make any type of paper, Arthur needs to know the 'grammage'.
The grammage is the mass of 1 m² of the paper, and is **directly proportional** to the **thickness** of the paper. The grammage and thickness of two of Arthur's paper types are shown below:

Print Grade
Thickness = 0.12 mm
Grammage = 80 g/m²

How to Make A Paper Aeroplane

Art Grade
Thickness = 0.15 mm
Grammage = 100 g/m²

a) Write a **formula** for Arthur to use to work out the grammage needed for any thickness of paper.

b) Arthur needs to make some paper **0.18 mm** thick. What **grammage** does he need?

c) Arthur thinks it would be useful to have a graph up in the factory which links thickness and grammage. Draw a suitable **graph** for Arthur.

Science in the Workplace

Q5 Jed works in a factory that makes aluminium foil.

The factory uses a radioactive detector to measure the thickness of the foil they make.

The detector works by measuring the percentage of radioactivity that can pass through the foil.

Jed uses the graph shown to check the thickness of foil from the detector readings.

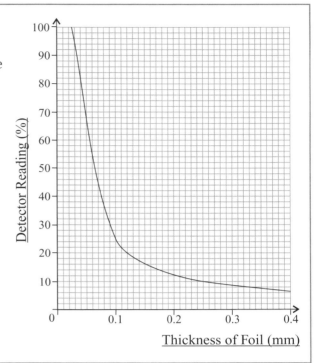

a) A new foil is supposed to have a thickness of **0.1 mm**. What reading should the detector show?

b) Jed wants to fit a warning light to the detector which flashes when the **foil thickness** is 10% above or below **0.1 mm**. What are the detector readings for these two limits?

Q6 Jed is testing a new detector. The detector reading is **inversely proportional** to the foil thickness. Jed puts a foil of a known thickness under the detector to find out how the two are linked:

a) What **equation** could Jed use to calculate foil thickness from the detector reading?

b) Jed wants to fit an alarm to the detector to go off when the thickness of the foil reaches **0.5 mm**. What reading on the detector should trigger the alarm?

Science in the Workplace

Q7 Natalie works in the safety testing department for a car manufacturer. She is testing the braking distance of a new car — the distance the car takes to come to a stop after the brakes are applied.

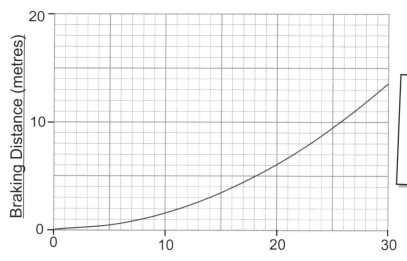

Results of Braking Distance Test in New Car:

If the car is braking correctly, the braking distance (B metres) should be linked to the speed of the car (S mph) by the equation:

$$B = 0.015\,S^2$$

Based on Natalie's results, do you think the new car is braking correctly?

Mirror... signal... manoeuvre...

Q8 Natalie needs to test the stopping distance of the car with a real driver.
She knows that typical 'thinking time' before applying the brakes is **0.675 s**.
The overall stopping distance is the thinking distance plus the braking distance.

If the car is braking correctly, the braking distance (B metres) should be linked to the speed of the car (S mph) by the equation:
$$B = 0.015\,S^2$$
Thinking distance (T metres) is calculated from the 'thinking time':
$$T = \textbf{Speed (m/s)} \times \textbf{Thinking Time (s)}$$
So the speed in mph must be converted to m/s first using the conversion:
$$1 \text{ mph} \approx \frac{4}{9} \text{ m/s}$$

Speed (mph)	Thinking Distance (metres)	Braking Distance (metres)	Overall Stopping Distance (metres)
0	0	0	0
10	3	1.5	4.5
20			
30			
40			
50			
60			
70			

Plot a graph of **overall stopping distance** against **speed** that Natalie could use to check her results.